NF2: Our Journeys

A collection of inspirational life stories written by people with NF2

Produced by Jessica Cook

First published in the United Kingdom in 2013

Title: NF2: Our Journeys
Subtitle: A collection of inspirational life stories written by people with NF2

Produced and published by: Jessica Cook
Production Assistant: Darren Osborne
Contact the publisher: http://canyouhearus.co.uk/contact-us

Printed by: The Lavenham Press Ltd, Arbons House, 47 Water Street, Lavenham, Suffolk CO10 9RN

ISBN: 978-0-9926112-0-0

Disclaimer:
All stories contained within this book are 100% authentic to the contributing author, who has consented to their stories being included in this book. Structural layout of stories may have occured to aid the flow of the book. All stories are in the contributors own words. NF2 is different for everybody. This book is not intended to act as medical or lifestyle advice and you should talk to your own NF2 clinician to discuss your own specific circumstances.

Contents

1. Introduction by Jessica Cook

**"The flower that blooms in adversity is
the rarest and most beautiful of all."**
(Walt Disney)

Underneath the surface of hardships, serious illnesses can also bring positive effects to a person's life; it can strengthen families, bring people together, and teach us things that we can only learn about once stripped of all the things we originally thought important in our lives (but actually weren't). It can encourage people to do the things they were either too busy or simply afraid to do.

Serious illnesses often force us to stop. To stop and reassess what is most important to us and to count our blessings. If we are strong enough physically, and strong enough in will and spirit, we get through those hard times and come out the other side a changed but better person.

Those with NF2 face both physical and mental challenges, but it can also open up the individuals' ability to enlarge on the gift of experiencing life from a new, challenging, exciting perspective. As someone who lives with NF2 I understand what it is like facing both surgery and the uncertainty of my future. But I know that there are amazing things out there in the world to see, amazing things to discover, amazing things to do, and amazing people to meet.

There is much more outside life with NF2, and this collection of life stories proves just that. It proves to others, as well as ourselves, that while we may have NF2, NF2 does not have us.

My journey – the producer

**"Why are you trying so hard to fit
in when you were born to stand out."**
(Ian Wallace)

So, who am I? I am Jessica Cook, and as I write this I am 23 years of age. I was diagnosed with NF2 at 8 years of age (1998) after my Mum began to seriously question why my left foot was significantly smaller than my right foot, and also why I was continually adopting a more obvious limp. An MRI scan revealed tumours in my lower spine which had restricted the growth of my left leg and foot; the tumours of NF2. Since then I have lived with multiple issues on my left side including a heavy foot drop, stunted growth, and conspicuous weakness. Balance loss and total sight loss in my left eye also add to the strains on my mobility.

Facial disfigurement has taken me on a journey of acceptance to a place where I no longer hide. A tumour attached to my left optic nerve not only caused total sight loss in my left eye but also became my most visible aspect of NF2 and the most frequently questioned part of my appearance. As the tumour grew it began to push my eyeball forward and cause the area of my face around my left eye to become severely swollen with fluid. What made things painfully difficult in my teenage years were the countless comments or questions from peers and strangers about the appearance of my left eye: "Oh my God! What happened?", "Who punched you?!". It was this type of questioning that caused me to withdraw not only from others, but from myself.

When I entered young adulthood and became more self-conscious of my appearance I got my fringe cut to a style that would completely conceal my left eye as a way of avoiding those hurtful questions and comments which were becoming a daily occurrence. But with time, I have begun to accept the appearance of my left eye. I now wear my fringe away from my eye, pinned back with a pretty clip or flower accessory. It was hard to stay strong and not return to my old ways when I began to receive the questions and comments again, but they no longer hurt me in the way that they used to. I came to some sort of realisation, over time. I figured if people couldn't accept me the way I was then they clearly weren't worth my time.

But the truth is; I wasn't accepting the way I was. How could I expect other people to accept me if I didn't accept myself? What's interesting is that since the revealing of my eye so many good people seem to have come my way. It proved to me that all I had to do was to give people the chance. I was so accustomed to the feeling of isolation that I was not letting people in, not allowing them to discover the whole Jessica Cook. So now, I have begun to be cut from the cords in which isolation bound me.

"The capacity for cure lies within each person"
(James Tighe)

Bilateral vestibular schwannomas (or VS/acoustic neuromas) were discovered a couple of years after my diagnosis. At age fourteen my annual MRI scan revealed that the time had come for my first surgery. I lost some hearing in that surgery, but some was also preserved by only partially removing the tumour. The schwannoma on my left hearing nerve had always been the bigger of the two and it was predicted that in time I would become completely deaf on this side; which inevitably happened after my second brain surgery in late 2007. After that surgery I was fitted with a hearing aid for my right ear which helped me in everyday life with communication and playing music.

Since the age of eleven I was very enthusiastic about music. I started by playing the saxophone and later learning the guitar. I formed my first band with three of my friends at age fifteen playing indie/pop music and later joined other bands playing ska, punk, rock, and contemporary folk music. Playing music was the biggest joy of my youth and it really hit me hard when shortly after graduating University and obtaining a degree in Popular Music and Record Production the remaining VS in my right ear began to grow again and my hearing rapidly decreased.

By mid-2011 my hearing loss had become so bad that I could no longer play my saxophone or guitar in any bands due to the loss of vital frequencies. At the time, I felt my days of playing in bands were not over. I was at my peak, the prime of my ability and passion, and I lost it. Although I accepted that I had to leave some things behind in the past, I couldn't accept that a future without music was my fate. Even after losing the majority of my hearing I still had the desire to be involved with music somehow, so I set about sourcing a solution. I could no longer hear the notation of melodic instruments so I moved my interest to the rhythm section and have now found a new passion in playing percussion.

Fate left me just enough hearing to motivate me into doing something more meaningful with music by sharing its magic with others. I now work as a volunteer aiding the development and skills of children and young adults with profound disabilities and complex learning needs through the provision of music therapy. I am now happier in my musical life than I ever was with good hearing.

**"Sometimes good things fall apart so
that better things can fall together"**
(Marilyn Monroe)

Sometimes we receive knocks that set us back a step or two, and then it's all about finding the strength to keep fighting. Living with NF2 has taught me the priceless skill of living in the present moment. I still have moments of worry about the future and nostalgia of the past, but they are not as extreme as they used to be when they took form of anxiety and depression. Those days are history, and I'm so thankful for that. It took a lot of hard work to begin to accept NF2 and the challenges it brought me. It can take a long time to find a level of acceptance that allows you to live in harmony with this condition, I wouldn't say I'm completely there myself yet, but I certainly feel myself improving.

NF2 has given me a life different to the norm, and for that I am thankful. It motivates me to challenge myself in a variety of ways, which perhaps people without the same difficulties do not. Whilst I acknowledge my difficulties I do not let them become barriers, and prefer to look at them from a different perspective. I consider my apparent weaknesses to be the catalysts of my strength. I like to do things to challenge them, to fight them, to spite them, and I say with total honesty that without NF2 and the challenges it has given me I would not have been the person that I am today. I don't think there is a more fulfilling or satisfying feeling than the conquering of your so-called limits, and I don't think there's anything more regretful than not at least trying.

More often than not bad things can be turned into good things, negative to positive, impossible to possible. It might mean not doing something the conventional way, but conventions are not rules. Sometimes, our so-called burdens can actually become our blessings.

Just as my hearing loss led me to my current volunteer work with music therapy, having my sight loss led me to Romania with a charity called Light Into Europe to work with children and young adults who have both visual and hearing impairments, living in a society that won't accept them. Having my balance loss and left leg weakness led me to the prominent hills of Northumberland and Cumbria to hike the full 84 miles of Hadrian's Wall in aid of the wonderful Willow Foundation. Having my NF2 led me to producing this book and making a positive change in the world.

A time of change

**"And that is how change happens.
One gesture. One person. One moment at a time."**
(Libba Bray)

Although my life outside of NF2 has always been full of fun and adventure - traveling to far off corners of the world, tearing about on horses at top speed, driving my car thousands of miles around the UK on spontaneous road-trips, attending college and university, playing music to my heart's content – it always felt like there was something missing. For so long I felt alienated and alone in what felt like a never ending battle with NF2. Even with the wonderful support of those around me, the feeling of being truly understood remained absent from my life until the day I met other people with NF2.

The first time I met other people with NF2 was at one of the fantastic Hearing Link Intensive Rehabilitation Programmes. It changed me, and I don't ever hold back from saying that. Finally someone understood what it was like to be me! Shortly after attending the programme I began a new drug treatment called Avastin (Bevacizumab) in the hope that it would either slow or stabilise a couple of very fast growing tumours. In the oncology unit I gradually began to spot others with NF2 and would spark a conversation with my new found confidence thanks to the Hearing Link Programme - and I should also mention here the "lucky" lady who most commonly attends infusions with me, my Nan Elaine..

Days in oncology are always long, which at first was draining, but soon it couldn't be long enough so that I could enjoy chatting the whole day away with the others. I started to look forward to days in oncology. The people I met there, and the people on the Link Programme, quickly became some of my dearest friends and I must thank them for being my rocks over the recent years and throughout my journey with this book. Of course though friendship is a huge bonus; sometimes simply just knowing of others can be a huge relief in itself. In one way or another, the importance of knowing others who are experiencing similar things has very clear benefits.

The Can You Hear Us? project

"You must be the change you wish to see in the world"
(Mahatma Gandhi)

Soon after meeting people with NF2 for the first time I decided to get involved with the NF2 online community. More and more people began to fall out of the woodwork, not just from the UK, but also internationally. It was after talking to these unbelievable people, seeing the kind of things they were achieving, and learning about their phenomenal determination to live life to the full that motivated me to create a way for them to be heard.

I simply could not just sit there and let them fade into history without telling their story; they had amazing things to tell, and amazing things to teach. I began to think about how I could make these people accessible so that others could have the same opportunity that I had, and not have to wait twenty-one years for it to happen. And so, I launched the Can You Hear Us? project and began to produce this book.

Can You Hear Us? is a self-help and social advocacy group on a mission to prove that there is more to life than NF2 through the uniting and presenting of people who refuse to be defined by the disease. Can You Hear Us? has been developed as a way of giving a voice to people with NF2 and to encourage those with the condition to take advantage of adversity.

The book

"We can't help everyone, but everyone can help someone"
(Ronald Reagan)

Every individual's journey with NF2 is different and the effects of the condition vary so vastly, which is therefore why a collection of stories is more powerful than one single story so that the reader is able to locate someone in which they can most personally relate to. At the beginning of each story you will find a short introduction stating simple facts about the author and what their story entails. How you read this book is up to you, but I hope that by including these introductions you will be able to access people more quickly with who you feel there is common ground and understanding.

Life with NF2 is a battle: but no battle is won without a fight. If you or someone who you love has been diagnosed with NF2, these stories will encourage and help you to develop attitudes and behaviours that these featured authors show. Let us never forget those here and elsewhere who have had the courage to overcome the challenges of adversity and have inspired others to do the same, and let us not forget that while NF2 may bring pain and suffering to individual lives, it has also brought out human goodness in those diagnosed and those around them. A guide to where to find further help and resources is available at the end of this book and also at the website www.canyouhearus.co.uk

So without further ado I give you the gift of, NF2: Our Journeys.

2. Adam Murdey

Adam Murdey is 40 years of age and lives in South Australia. Upon diagnosis of NF2 at the age of 14 Adam's dreams of a future in the Australian Forces seemed to shatter before him.

Despite a huge number of challenges thrown at him by NF2 Adam has achieved many qualifications in the area of administration.

Being a modest adrenaline junkie Adam's future looks set to be an exciting and adventurous journey.

I was diagnosed with NF2 as a fourteen year old, just over twenty-five years ago now (oh how time flies!!). The diagnosis not only turned my life upside-down in regards to my schooling but also what I wanted to do when I finished school.

Although there were no lofty grand visions of being the next front man for KISS (sorry, I'm an 80's child) and bumping Gene Simmons off his black platform boots or anything like that, but I did fancy being a policeman or joining the Royal Australian Air Force or even the army. But as we all know they do not accept people with a disability, especially deafness. They do, however, accept people with a disability to work in administrative roles. So this set the scene.

After completing Year 12 I enrolled in the local college and studied Business Administration – not exactly enthralling but it seemed like a good idea at the time. I was often told by well-meaning but clearly ignorant teachers that administrative work was good for deaf people to do because it's easy work and doesn't involve using too much of the old gray matter, "Great work for you, Adam. Would be ideal for you...." – no offence to those of you out there who do administrative work, I did it for many years and enjoyed it.

After finishing high school I attempted to enter University to study accounting (yeah I know, not exactly enthralling either) but because my grades didn't exactly set the academic world on fire I was not offered a place. This is why I continued on with the college courses for ten years and picking up contract work with various government departments, and also volunteering at various charities to help with their administrative work.

When I hit the big three-'O' I decided to have one more tilt at getting into Uni. Now over here in Australia there are many different ways to enter Uni: straight from high school - which depends on your final grade - mature entry, disability, or previous study, just to name a few. I applied using a few entry ways – hey, the more the merrier, right? Because of my previous four business administration certificates, my voluntary work history and my ripe old age (mature entry) they all went in my favour. A few quick wits, who received an equally quick ear clip from me, remarked that I'm the least mature person they know. Everybody's a comedian. I was eventually accepted in the Bachelor of Social Science course at the University of South Australia, otherwise known as UniSA.

I have received immense support from the disability support unit at UniSA throughout my degree. They have supplied interpreting support for lectures and tutorials and also a notetaker during lectures. This is a must for any deaf person attending lectures as it is near impossible to watch an interpreter, the lecturer and write notes.

I will be finishing my current degree in May 2013. It has been a hard slog, and in the ten years I have been studying I have had six lots of surgery. One surgery on my spine kept me in hospital and rehabilitation for almost six months and I am now an incomplete tetraplegic. This made me fall behind my peers and on many occasions throughout my degree it would have been easy to quit, people would have understood, but I didn't quit. If I had quit then I would have let NF2 win. NF2 would have got the better of me. If I had let it win and let it have the better of me then what next? If I came across another task that I found difficult because of what restrictions I now have due to NF2, would I quit that, too? With this thought I enrolled in another degree in 2012 while still at UniSA. The degree I'm studying is a (big breath) Bachelor of Disability and Developmental Education at Flinders University, which is also in South Australia. I am only studying one subject per semester until I have finished the other degree in May.

On a more personal note: A friend gave me a wonderful gift for my 40th birthday in June 2012.... a voucher to go tandem skydiving, which I did on 31st March 2013! I have had friends and family approach me saying skydiving is dangerous, you could get hurt, end up in a wheelchair (boom boom), etc. Well, when you live with NF2 it makes you realise how precious life is and not to waste one minute of it. I've travelled overseas twice, once to the UK to visit family and once to the US, so I have that out of my system, and so the skydiving will be my next challenge. What will I do after this? That's a mighty good question, I'm not sure exactly what quite yet, but I do know it will involve something just as adrenaline packed and worrisome for my Mum!

I don't let NF2 dictate my life or how I live my life. If I start doing that then it will take over and begin to stop me from doing the things I want to do.

I am going to finish off with a wonderful quote from Oprah Winfrey:

**"Nobody's journey is seamless or smooth.
We all stumble. We all have setbacks. It's just life's
way of saying, "Time to change course."**
(Oprah Winfrey)

To find out more about Adam you can visit his webpage http://users.cobweb.com.au/~ajmurdey/

3. Anna Lickley

Anna Lickley, from the UK, was diagnosed with NF2 in her late teens and is the first in her family to have the condition. In her story Anna tells us how she went about setting up her own business training in disability and deaf equality, and teaching BSL.

Even though Anna experienced difficulties in working towards her dreams she has found ways around those difficulties and has achieved despite them. Anna is also working on another promising project that will reveal a new NF2 book with a unique direction.

Well, I am 37 years old as I am writing this - with the body of a 92-year-old and the face of a teenager! The last two years or so have been some of the toughest so far for me in terms of trying to overcome an onslaught of NF2 related challenges.

I have had a cataract on my right eye since birth but as I was the first in my family to have the NF2 gene my own NF2 wasn't diagnosed until my late teens. As a result, doctors decided not to remove that cataract, not knowing that I would later go deaf through NF2 and now have damage on the cornea in my left eye, leaving me with scarring and very blurry vision. Lip-reading is next to impossible now, as are many everyday things. My balance is also much worse and I generally use a walking frame and cannot walk outside without help and guidance.

Communication wise I am greatly helped by the fact that at the time I went deaf (at university) I went to sign language and lip reading classes. I loved signing; I got to level 2 and later went on to learn level 3. In my early thirties I set up a business training in disability and deaf equality, and teaching BSL.

Setting up my own business was tough, but at the time not impossible. I went on a short training course that covered the essentials of setting up a business. The training providers funded communication support for me. I used a BSL interpreter but I also had the option of a lip-speaker or a manual/electronic note-taker.

In my previous work I'd learnt about Access to Work - a government-funded service to ensure that disabled people can have the same opportunities to work as non-disabled people. As a deafened person I was able to have communication support each time I provided training to others. I also got technology support such as a Minicom for contacting clients by phone using the Text Relay service, and a laptop to use if I was travelling for work.

It was always tough working, and my work was constantly interrupted by hospital visits and surgeries or MRI scans, making me tired and weaker. But working for myself allowed me to work around these times to some extent. Sadly I did embrace the need to close the business after my eyes went bad as I am also a great deal more tired and my balance is now such that I find just standing difficult and can only go short local distances.

I also had stereotactic radiosurgery for the second time in 2010 which initially made my tumours swell angrily giving me unbearable headaches and great tiredness. I have a fairly large meningioma and four other tumours in my head, two of which are pressing against and growing around my brainstem. There are also around fifteen or so smaller tumours in my spine.

Learning BSL has also given me lots of new friends, mostly hearing or deafened signers. This means that now, when lip-reading is not possible, I can still chat to others who know a bit of signing.

Over the years it has been a really great help and support to meet and get to know others who really know and understand this illness (i.e. people with NF2).

I can't say that having NF2 has taught me to appreciate and value life more, because I've always done that. But I have got more used to having it over time, adjusting and adapting to get as much from life as I can with the (sometimes endless seeming) challenges it brings. I feel more confident that life doesn't have to stop when living with an illness; it is just different (and often harder!).

When I stopped working I found the time to write a book, with the help of adapted technology. The book is written as fiction but is really about me and my life with NF2. It's currently with an agent.

I know this piece is fairly short but I have recently had further eye surgery making it a greater strain to type. However, I wanted very much to contribute to this book and hope it will be useful and encouraging to all of us NF2ers. I hope that you will be able to read a fuller account of my story if and when my novel gets published!

4. Beka Chanturia

Beka Chanturia has lived his whole life in the small country of Georgia, located at the crossroads of Western Asia and Eastern Europe. Unlike those of us living in Western cultures such as in the UK, America, and Australia, people residing in a country such as Georgia did not, and still do not, have access to the same high-standard of care that those in Western civilisations receive.

With a population of almost 4.5 million a basic calculation tells us that there must only be approximately 128 people with NF2 living in Georgia today, unfortunately most of which are unlikely to have yet been diagnosed. It is a place that desperately needs more awareness of NF2 and the people given hope and strength.

Beka has done an incredible thing for his country by sharing his honest testimony and inspirational grit. Through his struggles with NF2 Beka managed to graduate university with excellent grades and now works as an IT Auditor for a global leading company.

I don't know how and from where it came, but I have lived with NF2 all my whole life. As a child I could not understand why my mother could not hear while others could. She succumbed to unsuccessful surgery when I was ten years old. My grandma therefore looked after me from that age. My father has another wife and I have two little brothers and a sister. I love all of them very much, but everything could be better without this terrible disease.

My trouble started when I was six years old. I had gone to play tennis and my coach called my grandma to tell her that something was wrong with my leg. Doctors advised me to give up playing, to avoid running etc. I watched my friends playing football and basketball, but avoided to play as doctors suggested. I realized then that the only thing I was allowed to do was to have an inactive life.

I was twelve - thirteen years old when I noticed some strange feeling. I couldn't understand what it was so I applied to the doctors. They suggested that it was something like minor epileptic attacks, but according to an MRI scan I had something (a tumour) in my brain. There was no way out – surgery was ineffective and very risky in this case. Doctors offered me some medications, which I have been receiving for ten years already. Sadly, I cannot imagine my live without it.

I had surgery on my leg when I was fourteen years old. The surgery appeared to be not as successful as planned; however, thanks to it I now have less pain when walking. It was around this time when I realized that something I could do and was "allowed" to do was to study well. Despite doctors here in Georgia suggesting that I avoid mental activity as well as physical activity I entered one of the best universities in my country.

I tried to not pay attention to my problems and to live my life like any average teenager going to university and spending time with their group mates. During my time at university I was really troubled with my epileptic attacks. There were times when I was losing my mind, stayed unconscious, vomited, etc. But despite this I managed to obtain a good grade and affiliate friends. Unfortunately though, this was not to be the end of my challenges with NF2.

I was in the final year of my studies when one day I woke up with the feeling of numbness on the right side of my face. In the next day this feeling intensified and I was not able to chew my meal. I was also experiencing difficulties with my balance and felt weakness in other areas. That was the first time that I became afraid.

After two weeks of medical treatment I felt a bit better and as time passed I learnt to put up with my situation. The problems with my balance improved slightly but I noticed that I was starting to help my chin with my hand when chewing. Periodically I felt terrible pain in my face and the feeling of numbness spread all over it. This was followed by serious pain in my neck. Every morning I am troubled by this pain, I can't even sleep well because of it. There were plenty of nights that I spent sitting up on my bed because even painkillers were not able to kill may pain.

Through the pain and my other issues with NF2 I managed to graduate from university with high honour and then started to seek for a job. I thought that if had a job and work to do I would feel better and would at least had less time to dwell about my troubles. I had real difficulties in finding a job, but after several attempts I found an employer.

Now I work for a global leading audit company as an IT auditor. It gives me the feeling that despite NF2 I can do something, I am still important to someone outside of my family, and I am trusted with some work that even healthy people are not. I feel that despite some real problems I can still live a good and normal life.

There are many things that I love but am not allowed to do, but thanks God I have a loving family who really support me, and despite so many problems really care about me. At school and at university I met people who accepted me like I am and really supported me. I managed to learn something and to find a job. Everyday my work and sense of responsibility gives me the strength to feel well.

I am very upset that there is not yet a cure for NF2 and that I have to fight it myself, but thanks be to God that my family and I somehow manage to find the strength to fight it.

5. Ben Ryan

Ben Ryan, age 28 from Norfolk, England, inherited NF2 from his father. Ben's story is a wonderful tribute to his late father and recollection of the qualities and strengths passed from parent to son.

Witnessing the full extent of NF2 through his father was a heart-breaking experience for Ben, however, he now declares that whilst he has lost, he has also gained. Ben has shown immeasurable fortitude by sharing his father's story in the hope that it will reach out to others who have also suffered loss.

Whilst Ben remains hopeful for a brighter future his father will forever be honoured in this abiding acknowledgement of his courage to face the challenges of adversity.

Neurofibromatosis Type 2. I have been aware of the term for as long as I can remember. NF2 can be a hereditary condition as well as being a de novo mutation (spontaneous occurrence), which has a 50% chance of being passed onto offspring via the currently affected person.

My father was a Senior Aircraftman in the Royal Air Force. He was medically discharged shortly after I was conceived in 1985 for failing a hearing test. After pursuing the matter at his local hospital, he underwent a series of tests which subsequently discovered two brain tumours and after further testing he was diagnosed with Neurofibromatosis Type 2. His case was of the de novo variety; there was no history of the illness in our family whatsoever. He had surgery shortly after his diagnosis to remove a vestibular schwannoma and his condition escalated quite rapidly after that. Over a short period he was involved in numerous surgeries to help aid his condition which resulted in some good and bad repercussions.

A few years after his initial diagnosis and surgeries he suffered pronounced hearing loss and severe balance difficulties. Growing up as a small child experiencing this with two siblings was completely normal for all of us, we never knew any different. I was always made aware from as young as 5 years old that my father had a serious condition and supported him in any way possible. He felt completely normal to me and in no way did I feel different. He didn't actually need much support to begin with as he was always very adamant that his physical disabilities would never stop him living a conventionally normal life, which they did not. He tried to remain as physically active as possible, regularly exercising, travelling and just being generally active.

Further operations unfortunately left him paralysed down the left side of his body, resulting in him spending the rest of his life in a wheelchair and unable to see/hear. This happened over two decades ago though and surgeons now have a lot more experience and general awareness of the condition, so the likeliness of anyone experiencing these outcomes has massively reduced.

I was taught hand signing at the age of 8 years old so that I could communicate with my father. Both of us never saw this as a hindrance in anyway at all, it never even crossed our minds that it would affect our relationship, and it didn't. He was a great teacher to me and in some ways I feel that the intimacy that usually comes with signing helped in that sense.

My father encountered many more issues with the illness as his physical health slowly deteriorated over the years. Many less obvious problems began to appear, for instance, he was unable to open up his hand due to schwannoma growths and nerve damage, resulting in communication becoming very difficult as his open hands needed to be used. The ability to perform simple tasks to provide self-care also slowly diminished.

The switch from him needing semi to full-time care eventually came and he left his sons' home town of King's Lynn for Ovingdean, Brighton, to join the St Dunstan's centre for visually impaired veterans. The care he received was magnificent, not to mention the lovely view of the English coast. Even with his health continuing to decline he was aided on "days out" to places such as the Duxford war museum where he was still able to impress people with his knowledge of aircraft he had the fortune to work with in previous years.

He had the opportunity to meet some true war heroes at St Dunstan's which entertained him for the remainder of his life. Unfortunately, after a few years, he contracted pneumonia and passed away on July 15th, 2007, at the age of 46.

I was diagnosed with NF2 at the age of 12. Me and my two brothers were tested and had a 50/50 chance of inheriting the condition from my father. My younger brother and I drew the short straws. My father blamed himself for my situation, which I'm sure is only natural for any parent, but I didn't blame him whatsoever.

Upon discovering the diagnosis, I wasn't affected by it at all. I was well aware of what managing the condition was like. My father's attitude whilst living with NF2 imbued me with strength and the knowing that there is no need for resignation or to lack hope of having a normal conventional life like any of the other children around me. Part of this belief came from experience and also partly from my father's blatant refusal to be affected by his condition. I don't remember my father ever once complain about anything related with NF2 (life-style or pain related).

I took a very similar approach in my own life; I let NF2 take a "back seat". After my diagnosis I regularly attended annual hearing/visual tests as well as annual MRI scans to monitor my development, but aside from that I carried on living a perfectly normal life until my first surgery to remove a vestibular schwannoma.

A while after the vestibular schwannoma on my right side was removed I was offered a new course of drug treatment named Avastin to try and help manage tumour growth and hopefully preserve hearing. I started this treatment in 2011 and it has helped to stabilise my tumour growth thus far. I know this isn't a cure but it certainly offers a sign of hope.

NF2 has sometimes made me feel a sense of worthlessness, especially after seeing my father pass away. I've had feelings of "why bother to carry on?" and I've self-destructed. However, recently NF2 has led me to meet others who share the same condition and cope amazingly well with it and that in itself has helped my self-esteem so much, I wouldn't change that for the world. I think it is very important to talk about, and share with other people the things you are feeling. For so long I bottled things up and tried to cope on my own, but I now realise that it does not have to be that way.

As NF2 is such a rare condition, I feel that people don't always understand the problems we encounter to the full extent and can become misguided. But talking to others who have the condition themselves has been so much help to me, as I feel they understand on a level that people without the condition cannot.

For many years I viewed NF2 as such a big negative in my life and I never drew any positives from it whatsoever. I viewed it as a constant ticking time bomb, but over time I have learned that there are positives from it. I have met some wonderful and inspiring people along my journey and it has changed my life in a hugely positive way.

6. Bethany

Bethany is 20 years of age and was diagnosed with NF2 at the tender age of 10. Bethany talks about acceptance of her current situation and, as a Jehovah's Witness, enlightens us with her hopes and beliefs for a brighter future.

At the age of 4 years old something wrong was detected by my parents in my right leg. It just wasn't functioning as it should when I walked, causing me to stumble. This gradually worsened as I grew up. Doctors and physicians were unable to explain the cause of this, until finally, six years later, all was revealed. It came as quite a shock, especially to my parents.

I was diagnosed with Neurofibromatosis Type 2 at 10 years old after an MRI scan was taken and revealed a large tumour in my brain, with other smaller tumours surrounding it. This also explained the cause of the palsy in my leg and foot. I had tumours on my spine that had damaged my nerves but it was too late to do anything for my leg by then, taking the tumour away would do nothing.

I had immediate surgery to install a shunt that would allow the fluid to run from my head that had been gathering on my brain due to the tumour, causing a lot of pain. Three weeks later, I had the tumour removed. I had quite a long recovery period, where I missed a lot of school and other activities. I had facial weakness after the last operation, which I remember didn't bother me much; at such a young age, it seemed so trivial. It slowly came back in time anyway.

Three years later, when I was 13, it was decided that I would have an Auditory Brainstem Implant installed at the same time as another brain tumour was to be removed which would take all of my hearing away completely. I was reluctant to have the Implant at first, not knowing how it would be. I expected it to sound horrible and mechanical. In the end though, I realized it would be the only way I could have some hearing at all.

In those past three years my hearing had rapidly deteriorated, and my confidence along with it. I remember being quite an outgoing young girl, but as I began to see that I couldn't keep up with my peers my confidence dimmed down. It was a very sensitive age for it to happen to me, and it changed my life. I had to learn to change with it. Communication with others became increasingly difficult; I felt very isolated at times. I had been learning Sign Language in that time and loved it! It means so much to me now; it has brought me closer to so many people. Along with that, I do appreciate my ABI very much. It has worked so well for me; it was more than I ever expected it to be. It has made it possible to have an everyday conversation with people, not always very easily, but it is still a little miracle to me. I am so grateful for it. I was told I'd be unable to hear music ever again, but that is not so! I still get to enjoy music very much!

After this operation, I had facial weakness again, and this time I noticed it more. Looking back now I'm surprised it didn't upset me more, or make me feel really self conscious. Again however, I gained movement back in my face. It is still a little bit weak now, but it doesn't bother me anymore.

Being Deaf and having foot drop also affects my balance greatly. I hate walking outside on my own, I fear I'll trip or wobble every five seconds, which I usually do! I have a leg splint which helps, but walking alone can seem like the toughest challenge sometimes. It's not really embarrassing to me anymore, I've learnt to laugh at myself a bit and just carry on.

When I was 18, I began experiencing a lot of pain deep in my back from a tumour on my spine. They were quick to operate on it, remove the tumor, and it brought me immediate relief! For 4 months I had been sleeping on a reclining chair in my living room; I couldn't lay flat on a bed because of the amount of pain I was in at that time. I was at home a lot during this time; it restricted my ability to walk and so on. I remember feeling very emotionally affected, I felt left behind with what others were doing around me, I felt somewhat useless. I wasn't expecting such good results from the surgery, but it brought me so much relief! The first night I was able to come home, I was back in my bed again! It's amazing how much we can take for granted. Later in that same year I had Stereotactic Radio Surgery, or Gamma Knife as it is sometimes called, on another brain tumour that was beginning to cause me discomfort. I suffered a great deal of pain after this procedure due to complications that were unexpected by us all. But now, almost a whole year later, the surgery is proving successful. The tumour has shrunk by a few millimeters, and will continue to keep shrinking. I am definitely feeling the effects of it now! That was my last surgery to date, and hopefully, the last for a while.

Every MRI scan I have is painful, because of the magnet in my implant; I feel the magnetic pull of it. Of course though I must have scans regularly to keep check of everything, and so I have anesthetic injected in my head around the magnet and then a bandage wrapped tightly around my head with a plastic card to keep the magnet in place. The first time I had this without any anesthetic was quite traumatic for me. It put me off having any more scans. Now however, I kind of brace myself up for it, and it turns out fine. The results of the scans are usually quite positive, but there is always a plan of action if something needs to be done. This puts my mind at ease when I know I am in safe hands.

I have been diagnosed with NF2 for ten years now - too many. It may sound like quite a frightening condition to have due to its unpredictable nature, but I don't feel afraid of what is only possible to happen. I am just aware of what could happen, but try to be positive. I have been so well looked after by the NF2 teams and I feel everything is kept under control. I do rely on others sometimes quite a lot in social gatherings and so forth.

When it comes to communication I sometimes need someone to help me out because I am Deaf. This does make me feel quite distant from people sometimes as they hesitate to talk to me out of fear they'll embarrass themselves, or even me. It can also take away my sense of independence, having to rely on other people in this way.

I remember being in a room with one of the surgeons and my parents when I was 10, and as my hearing was already not great by then, all I really got from the conversation they were having was that I had a brain tumour that needed to be removed. As I knew almost nothing about why I had the tumour, and what it would mean, hearing this did scare me. At that age, all the things I'd heard in the past about brain tumours were frightening, and now I had some of my own. It was quite surreal. As time did go on however, I began to accept things. Being Deaf was probably the hardest thing to accept because it would affect nearly everything I did in everyday life, and I feared I'd become some sort of an outcast. I definitely do not feel that way anymore. I still wish I could hear perfectly, but I have accepted that is what life is at the moment. I say "at the moment" because I believe in something very much, something that has helped me in every step of my life, something that has seen me through every tribulation and helped me to come through as a stronger person. I am one of Jehovah's Witnesses, and I have a very beautiful hope for the future that one day, along with many others, I will have perfect health and no more worry of ever being ill again. That is what I look forward to, and that is what keeps me going.

I hope what I've had to say will be helpful to whomever reads this, whether you're a person with NF2 yourself, or somebody that knows someone with the illness. I hope that it has given some insight to what it is like living with it. I think people prove everyday that they can live their life the best they can, and see something positive in any situation. Having NF2 doesn't make us any different; we can still live a good life, and be happy and hopeful.

7. Bruno R Tamassia

Bruno R Tamassia is 35 years of age and from San Paolo, Brazil. Bruno had symptoms of NF2 since 8 years of age but was not diagnosed with the condition until age 18. Upon diagnosis Bruno struggled to find any NF2 related information in Brazil to answer the hundred questions of his worried mind.

Later, in order to benefit others in a similar situation, Bruno established an NF Foundation called Associaçao de Neurofibromatose and website www.neurinoma.com.br to provide the people of Brazil with access to information about NF2.

Bruno claims that having NF2 has changed his perspectives on life and in his story explains how this has not only had a positive impact on him, but also others.

I have been living with NF2 for about twenty-seven years now. I had my first symptoms when I was 8 years old. I had a slight facial paralysis on my right side and the doctors spent a lot of time trying to discover what was happening with me.

I had my first surgery at nine years old and my second one at twelve years old, but NF2 was not diagnosed until I began to lose part of my hearing at eighteen years old. I had an MRI scan which revealed the bilateral acoustic neuromas. When the doctors told me about NF2 they did not explain that it can be like a monster! They just told me that I would need annual MRI scans and to pay close attention to any new symptoms.

Brazil is a very poor country but I fortunately had the opportunity of being born into a family with good financial support to help me through the battles of NF2. I have had some of my surgeries done in the USA with the most experienced doctors in world, so the ability to finance this has helped me a lot.

When I was given the diagnosis of NF2 I felt worried and I started to read and study about the condition. In Brazil we did not have any information about acoustic neuromas and NF2 then, so I decided to create a web site (www.neurinoma.com.br) and a NF Foundation called Associaçao de Neurofibromatose.

Both of my acoustic neuromas were operated on within six months of each other and the surgeons managed to preserve much of my hearing by leaving behind some small pieces of the tumours. I did lose some function from the facial nerve on my right side in this surgery, but I continued hearing for a further seven years.

After recovery from the major surgeries I continued on with my life. I worked hard and often and also finished my studies, graduating in Business Administration. One year after the surgeries my MRI scan revealed that both of the remaining acoustic neuromas had begun to grow again. It sounded like game-over to me, I was sure at that moment I would die someday soon, and it hurt me a lot.

When you have a progressive disease you have only two options: stop or go ahead. I decided to go ahead. Not only that, but to accelerate my life. In three years I achieved two Masters Degrees and I started to raise money to begin the Brazilian NF Foundation.

In the beginning, when NF2 started to affect me, I searched for support in religion. But, thanks to my ex-girlfriend, I saw that really I needed psychotherapy support in order to accept the challenges that NF2 could bring. Today, I have had therapy for about ten years. I like it, and it helps me a lot.

I am the first one in my family to have NF2. Losing my hearing affected my quality of life quite a lot as I lost a good job because of it. But I never give up, and I always try to do the things I want by finding another way. Today I have a web-shop and I work with my favourite hobby - Model Cars.

I hate hospitals. So far I have had five separate brain surgeries, one radiosurgery, and two surgeries to my right eye. I have always tried to channel my bad feelings into doing something positive and helping other people. When I began to do that, things became easier for me to accept, and always I am looking for a reason to fight and go on.

After my most recent surgery I decided to invite the doctors who did my ABI to Brazil so that they could teach the Brazilians doctors some of their skills. It makes me happy to know that although I have had a lot of pain in my life the cause of that pain has provided me with the perspective to help others, more specifically the less privileged people in my country. Today we have over ten ABI users in Brazil that would have never dreamed of having such a thing until I had my surgery.

The loss of hearing and balance has much impact on my life and in the lives of those beside me. But how I see myself has the same impact too. Loving yourself is the first and most important thing. I still have my friends that I had before things with NF2 started to happen; they stuck close by me and have supported me throughout my journey. I also still do most of the things that I did as a hearing person, but it is sometimes hard as every day I need to recharge my batteries and start everything over again.

Since I was diagnosed with NF2 my life has changed a lot. The things that I once believed to be important I now see are not so important. I live in the present moment, and I need to accept that I will not have the same type of life that people without NF2 have.

I have a lot of tumours in my spine and I am not sure what will come of them, but I have no control over that. What I can control is taking care of myself through things such good nutrition, body exercises, and looking after my mind.

I have been married for eight years now - yes, I had married as a deaf person, hard, but not impossible. Fortunately my wife has no problems with her health and we have two children. The first child, Fred, is her first married son, and our daughter of five years we used In vitro fertilization (IVF) to avoid her being born with NF2.

I am a happy guy in general, but not always of course. I wrote my life history with my hands and I continue to believe in drugs and new NF treatments. Despite having NF2 I realized most of my dreams; I did my study and achieved my graduation, I wrote a book, I married, and I am the father of a Princess.

I love my life. I have a lot of hobbies; I love riding horses, I love slot-cars and model radio control cars, and I love good books, the list could go on. I really don't like TV; I don't have time to spend in front of it because I need to live! I dream to live on a farm, until now I cannot but I continue to hope that one day my family and I will. Loving your life is one of the most important things that I learnt with the support of my family.

8. Claire Middleton

Claire Middleton was diagnosed with NF2 in early 2002 at the age of 20. Claire lives in Essex, UK, and is now 31 years of age. Her story shows us that although life with NF2 can be an emotional roller-coaster it is still possible to be happy through the ups that life brings.

Claire stresses that family and friends play a vital role in guiding you on your journey and how setting yourself small goals through something such as a hobby can bring significant benefits.

I must point out first that no one else in my family has NF2. It all started in early 2001 when I was having problems hearing in my right ear. My GP told me it was just fluid behind the ear drum and told me to come back in three months' time. So three months later with no improvement I went back. He told me there was still fluid there so come back in another three months. Well, this went on for nine months with no signs of improvement.

Then out of the blue I received an appointment for an MRI scan at my local hospital. I had the scan and then about two months later I got to see a consultant who couldn't tell me what was wrong but referred me to another hospital, which was 70 miles away. So in October 2002, just 10 days before my 21st birthday, I was told I had Neurofibromatosis Type 2. My fiancé - now husband - and my life seemed to just drop from a great height. I broke down and my poor husband was in absolute shock. At first I wondered what I had done wrong in life to deserve this kind of news, but as the days went on I knew I was still me, so I vowed to never let this condition drag me down.

I had my first tumour removed in 2004. The tumour was on my spinal cord and had been causing me great pain since I was in my teens. It was during that recovery that I took up cross stitching as a hobby. I have been doing it ever since and have never looked back from the hobby. I suppose that cross stitching is really one of the good things that came out of this medical condition.

I eventually lost 60% of my hearing by early 2004 and I had to have a hearing aid in my left ear. I had the first acoustic neuroma removed in 2005 on the right side so through that operation I lost all hearing on the right side, as well as losing balance too. In the same operation I had an Auditory Brainstem Implant (ABI) fitted which is absolutely fantastic for me.

I remember that no one would let me have a mirror to see myself because the surgeon also found that my facial nerve had a tumour on so the nerve had to be cut in order to remove the entire tumour. When my family and husband came to see me after the operation they saw that my head was so swollen that you couldn't see my ear, and the left side of my face dropped. But one thing that I still think about today and will never forget was the look of love in my husband's eyes.

2006 was the hardest time of our lives because in the middle of the year I had suffered with headaches and sickness for three days. My husband contacted my consultant/neurosurgeon and he had an ambulance come and get me straight away. Once they got me back to the hospital I was scanned and they found that I had a tumour in the centre of my brain and it was pushing on my brain stem. I don't think I'd be alive today if my husband hadn't phoned the hospital.

I had a strip of hair shaved along the top of my skull during the operation for them to be able to do the surgery and, I have to be honest here, I found it highly amusing a few months later. I had long hair at the time and as the hair was growing back the shaved strip of hair was short and spiky. I said it looked like I had a Mr T hair style but the wrong way round. I found that having a laugh like that helped me deal with it.

Between 2004 and 2009 I have had nine NF2 related operations. I know I have more to go but I take each day at a time and whatever NF2 throws at me I face it head on.

We decided not to have children because neither of us wants to see our children go through what I've been through. I know there's a 50/50 chance of them not having NF2 but for me personally that is too high - but everyone's opinion is different.

NF2 has made life have more downs than ups, but we can still enjoy life. It's comforting to know that there are more people out there in the world going through similar things - it's nice to know that we're not alone in this. If it hadn't of been for my close friends, and family, my mother-in-law and most of all my husband, I don't think that I could have carried on much longer. They have all helped me so much and it means the world to me.

9. Claire

Claire, age 33 from Kent, UK, inherited NF2 from her father and was diagnosed at the age of 14. In her story Claire talks about now being proud to be a deaf person and even how she has now made a career out of it.

Claire also gives an insight into her thoughts and feelings of the moment when she met someone else with NF2, other than her late father, for the first time. She explains how it was a very emotional journey for her but now realises the benefits it can bring, so in turn, decided to share her story in this book in order to provide others with that same opportunity.

To me deafness is not a problem.

I inherited NF2 from my dad. I was 14 years old when I was diagnosed, it was too late to save any hearing in my left ear but I had stereotactic radiosurgery on my right ear to save some hearing. Over seven years this did decrease anyway and I now have very little hearing in my right ear. I also get tinnitus, which is constant, and my balance isn't so great.

My story is a long one and I cannot possibly go into too much detail. I grew up with an amazing mum and dad. I never knew my dad to be hearing and so growing up with him being deaf was normal to me. Perhaps this is why I took losing my hearing in my stride because I had such a great role model, and at the end of the day it was going to happen no matter what I did!

As I said, losing my hearing, although scary and an emotional roller coaster, is not the problem. The NF2 disease and the uncertainty it brings is the main problem. I know that nothing in life is easy and everything has a risk, but living with NF2 really does scare me and I would be lying if I said any different. I get on with life and I don't let NF2 stop me, but it is a cloud that is always there.

Looking back, my mum suggested I learn sign language. Dad didn't like this as he wanted me to stay as independent as possible; he also had quite an old fashioned view on things. I was a typical stroppy 15 year old and even though the doctors said "you will eventually be completely deaf" I just didn't believe them at that time and thought I'd just deal with it IF and when it happened. But mum being as sensible and amazing as she is thought it was best I prepare before it happened.

Anyway after a few debates and a lot of teenage tantrums I learnt very basic communication signs with mum. I continued to lip-read all the time as it made certain situations so much easier, although at first I hated it and did try to stay "hearing". It took a good few years to be able to say "sorry I can't hear you". My dad made me promise to stay talking and lip-reading to keep my independence and I have kept that promise to this day. Although learning sign language as early on as I could is probably the best thing I have ever done.

My hearing took a dive, and rapidly declined over just a few months. I was suddenly in a world of silence, everything was moving but not making sound – apart from the ringing and buzzing that is tinnitus of course.

Fast-forward several years; I am now 33 and proud to be a deaf person. I carried on learning sign language and am now fluent. I've also met some amazing friends in the Deaf community and have even made a career out of it. I gathered I may as well make some money out of this horrible condition if nothing else! I work as an employment, information, advice and guidance consultant for Deaf and deafened people; assisting them to prepare for or enter work, whichever stage they are at in their life.

I have done a lot of travelling: Australia, Thailand, Hong Kong, America. And then, I married my best friend. He carries me through the dark times I do have when NF gets me down. We have a great life; a house, good jobs, a dog and a cat, and we live every day for what it is.

I am now having Avastin therapy and this is bringing me hope for the future. A cure for NF would be a miracle but until then if we can treat the condition and keep it under control then I think that is amazing and good enough for me! Avastin is bringing me physical benefits as well as emotional ones.

NF2 can bring so much uncertainty, pain and sadness to people's lives. I know that I am constantly worrying about my future. I had never met anyone else apart from my dad with NF until I was referred to the NF2 centre in London. I had many mixed emotions that day; I was scared, emotional, and nervous. But in a strange way I was excited because I knew that there was help for me out there and after losing my dad, I wasn't alone anymore. As I always say, hey I'm special, I'm one in 35,000!

10. Craig Briscoe

Craig Briscoe was diagnosed with the mosaic form of NF2 in his late twenties. Craig is now 39 years of age and lives in West Yorkshire, UK. In his story Craig talks about his decision to start a family. He also gives us an insight into some of his personal interests including technology, engineering, and motorsport.

My name is Craig, I'm 39 years old and I live and work in the UK. I am married with a 5 year old daughter. I have a mosaic form of NF2. I am currently profoundly deaf in one ear, with moderate – severe loss in the other.

Step back in time to 1996 when at the age of 22, a routine hearing test at work indicated some loss in my left ear. After an initial visit to my GP and then a referral to the local ENT centre, I was sent for a precautionary MRI scan. It was after this scan that I was first diagnosed with bilateral acoustic neuroma, or vestibular schwannoma as we now call them. Much frantic activity ensued and a referral to a larger ENT department. My head was left spinning as I contemplated regular MRI scans to monitor the tumours, the possibility of total hearing loss and even future brain surgery – I can't even cope with needles! This was a worrying time as I didn't know what to expect for the future. Would I go deaf? When might it happen? How might I cope? The prospect of that kind of surgery scared me silly.

I was accompanied then and have been ever since, to pretty much every appointment by my wife Joanne. We had literally just moved in together, and we married in 1997.

The yearly MRI scans to monitor the tumours, as well as the obligatory hearing tests, showed little or no change for several years. Although the hearing loss in my left ear progressively worsened, my right ear remained good, allowing me for the most part to continue leading a normal life. To some extent I managed to forget about the whole thing, although turning a deaf ear was occasionally useful!

At some point in the early 2000s, probably around 2003, my neurosurgeon suggested investigating the possibility of a genetic link to the neuromas, thus leading to the eventual diagnosis of NF2. Taking it one stage further, it was also confirmed to be the mosaic form, being triggered at some point in my early development by a random mutation, and I could at least hope for any effects to be lesser than if the condition had been full blown. This also implied that there was no previous family occurrence. To be honest, this did nothing for me other than give an explanation for what was going on, but did introduce the possibilities of other complications – such as passing the condition on.

Life continued as normal. MRI scans – incidentally I don't mind these, apart from having the line inserted to inject the dye. I hate that - hearing tests, results. No change. I'd say I was a little naïve towards NF2 at this time, as it wasn't particularly having a detrimental effect on my everyday life. I was happily going along working as an engineer, socialising with family and friends, and so on.

In around 2006 we decided we wanted to try for a family, and we were offered genetic testing to give us a risk factor of me passing on the condition. This came back as a quite encouraging 'less than 5% chance'. Roll on to 2008 and our new baby daughter Holly burst onto the scene. I don't think a day passed since she was conceived that I didn't contemplate the possibility of her having NF2, and the implications that it would have on her future, considering that if it had been passed on, she could experience the effects much worse than I had myself.

Doctors initially advised against testing her at a young age for NF2, since any effects of the condition are not generally seen until late teens / early adulthood. Putting her through any of the tests as a child seemed unnecessary. Although this did little for our peace of mind, we accepted that it was for the best.

My MRI scan in 2010 showed growth of the tumour on my right hand side – my good ear. It was at this point that intervention in the form of Gamma Knife (Stereotactic Radiotherapy) surgery was suggested. This was deemed the most appropriate action since my tumours were too small for removal by conventional surgery, and although not without risk Gamma Knife statistics offered the best possibility of preserving some level of hearing. In late 2010 I attended my initial consultation for Gamma Knife surgery, expecting to receive treatment sometime in the following year. Since I am fairly close to the treatment hospital I also opted to go on the waiting list for any cancellations. So, imagine my surprise after starting a brand new job in the new year of 2011, I got the call for a cancellation and found myself undergoing the surgery at the end of February. Luckily my new boss was (and still is) understanding and supportive.

I can't lie, that particular experience wasn't the most pleasant in the world, but I can't even imagine the alternative. I didn't feel terribly great immediately afterwards, but this soon passed. I suspect the procedure may have caused me a few balance issues in the following few months, but again, my grey matter seems to have taken account of this and it rarely bothers me anymore.

My hearing was still good on that side immediately after surgery, and was for around a year afterwards. Persistent tinnitus had also set in a year or two earlier, but this was reasonably easy to ignore for the most part with that right ear still working well. Then the hearing started to deteriorate. It started at the higher frequencies initially, and is gradually getting worse from there as time progresses. So, since early 2012 I have been using hearing aids in both ears. The tinnitus continues and does now add to the difficulty as it masks what good hearing I do still have. I tend to notice it less when I'm busy doing something, but it is ever present.

In 2012 we did end up getting Holly tested, and to our massive relief she got the all clear. I will never be able to articulate how elated this made me feel – yes, there were tears! Knowing she doesn't have this condition lifted such a huge weight from me. We got this news shortly before attending a NF2 Intensive Rehabilitation Programme, organised by Hearing Link in the UK. This was my first ever encounter with other NF2 patients. Honestly, it was a bit of a shock. I had no idea it could cause such problems, making my daughter's recent test results all the more poignant. It also made me feel rather lucky in comparison – even almost a bit of a fraud to be considered in the same group as those guys. I met some great people there who I now consider friends and it was a very interesting and informative week. I can recommend attending.

Back to the present, and I am currently waiting to see if I am suitable for a cochlear implant in my left ear, the one that hasn't really worked for such a long time. I can't say that I'm looking forward to the prospect of such a procedure, but if the outcome is positive it will be well worth it. Pretty much my biggest concern is being able to continue working. I enjoy my job and hope to keep doing it for as long as I can, and obviously I need to support my family by earning a living.

Being a bit of a techno geek I have embraced technology. I recently installed a loop system at home so I can enjoy the TV to an extent with my hearing aids – although I do still rely on subtitles. I have similar things for listening to radio and music. Through Access To Work, my employer has provided me with listening devices for attending meetings and using my phone. Not all is perfect, but it is way better than nothing. My work colleagues are mostly very understanding and with a little honest guidance from me have adapted well as to how best to communicate with me. I can also honestly say that all encounters outside of the office relating to my work have all been very positive. People have been very understanding of my situation and responded accordingly.

It's hard to comprehend how much you rely on your hearing for so much, if not everything. Even when it is failing, you automatically try and rely on what little is left. The feeling of isolation can occasionally creep up too, the feeling that you're missing out on things. I have been learning to lip-read for some time now, and although I don't find it very easy it helps a great deal. We are starting on a British Sign Language course very soon as well. I hope this will not become my primary mode of communication, but it will be useful to have under my belt, even if we just use it when we are out and about when background noise and such like can make communication difficult. I've heard it said many times but I think it's much harder to adjust to losing hearing (or any sense for that matter) than never having had it at all. It has indeed made life more challenging, right from the simplest of things to the most important things.

Simple things – like watching the TV or listening to the radio in the car. Making a phone call. Having a chat. Important things – like trying to understand something that my little girl is excitedly trying to tell me about or ask me...

So there it is. NF2 has not really played a huge part in my life until very recently. But now it is here it looks like it will continue to make life challenging in the future. My intention is to continue as best I can, enjoying life with my family, watching and supporting my daughter as she grows up and develops. To keep working to the best of my ability.

Joanne and I, along with Holly, are a pretty tight family unit. We holiday in the UK and just enjoy doing stuff together.

I work as an engineer mainly involving electronics, computers and vehicles. I have always been that way inclined. How does stuff work? How can I fix it? Consequently, I ended up getting into computers and such, and much to my wife's continued dismay I like endlessly tinkering with things! I think this attitude has helped me deal with my situation – I can't do anything about it, so I won't worry. Too much.

Cars and motorsport are other things I love. I have always enjoyed music and films, am a self-confessed Sci-fi and fantasy nerd and a total Star Wars fan boy. I love the works of Tolkien and Peter Jackson's translation of these onto the big screen. These pastimes are more difficult with hearing loss. Subtitled DVDs are great, but the cinemas are less inclined to offer much choice in this area. Music I miss the most. I still hope to master playing the guitar while I can still hear something, somehow...

One thing I have taken to recently is running. Aside from a desire to maintain some sort of fitness, this has partly been down to my failing hearing. I find myself thinking that if something is going to stop working and I can do nothing about it, then I'll make sure everything else is in good shape! Who knows how it might progress, I have no real desire to compete in marathons, but I do fancy taking part in the Great North Run if I can get to the right level. Perhaps raise a bit of money for the likes of Hearing Link. We'll see how my ageing knees hold out, years of abuse by football might get in the way!! Maybe I'll even try new things... no idea what new things until they come along.

11. David

David of Hampshire, UK, was diagnosed with the mosaic form of NF2 at 61 years of age, he is now age 74.

In his story David tells us how although he has not yet had any form of treatment for NF2 that the "wait and watch" method of management can be an anxious time. David also informs us of the wonders of communication aids and other useful adaptations in and around the home.

Hi, my name is David and I was diagnosed with NF2 in the year 2000 when I was 61 years old. Obviously I had it before but it was only diagnosed then. It took the NHS over two years from my first symptoms to carry out an MRI scan which showed two tumours in my head. The larger tumour on my left side very quickly caused the total loss of hearing on that side. On the right side there is a much smaller tumour but about 50% of my hearing has now gone on that side. I find speech discrimination very difficult and have problems understanding anyone who has an accent or poor diction.

To date I have not been given any treatment although originally surgery was offered, however a second opinion at another hospital advised a "wait and watch" policy. Several other tumours have since been found, one on a facial nerve and three on the spine. I have a fair bit of spasmodic pain which only a combination of pain killers, including morphine, can deal with.

During the time I have had NF2 there have been balance issues which are at their worst when I am tired and when the lighting levels are poor. Walking takes more effort than normal as more energy is expended in an effort to stay upright and to walk in a straight line. Quite bad tinnitus has been with me for over twenty years and at times it is quite difficult to tolerate but there isn't any choice or cure, I believe this is linked to the NF2. A masker for tinnitus was issued to me, which rarely seems to help; one snag is that it cannot be used in conjunction with a hearing aid.

I quite strongly believe the genetic damage later in my life causing the NF2 was by being exposed to various forms of nuclear radiation. This occurred mainly in the mid-eighties having at times to evacuate situations very quickly as the maximum dose rate was reached in a very few minutes. The government and nuclear authorities of course say this cannot be proved, so no recognition, help or compensation whatsoever.

To help with communication, I have for several years attended a lip-reading class. This is normally just once a week for 2 hours. Although the lip-reading class is subsidised, there is a £60 annual fee in my area. The lip-reading class is very enjoyable and great fun and it is good to mix with others with deafness or a hearing problem, but I still find lip-reading very hard and consider myself a very poor lip reader.

For my right ear I have a hearing aid which does not seem to help much but is useful in some situations. I find it very difficult to communicate in social groups, it is very difficult to contribute, as I do not understand what is being said or what is discussed. This has made me very much a one to one person. I find it necessary to always have some light, even at night, to help me with disorientation in the dark.

To date I have had 17 MRI scans- 14 head and 3 spinal. Very strangely as time has gone on I have become more and more claustrophobic and now need to take Temazepam and Diazepam one hour before having a MRI scan. I use Diazepam occasionally to ward off panic attacks. Other than severe pain the other worse thing for me is a panic attack. You have to experience a panic attack to understand the feelings it evokes – very scary. Fortunately these are few and far between.

Before I was diagnosed with NF2 it became necessary to retire early due to communication problems which included not understanding what was being said on the telephone. I can no longer use a normal telephone, but now have one with a powerful speaker; there is then of course an issue with confidentiality. When watching TV or listening to the radio I had to have the volume so loud it made it unbearable to anyone else. I now use a single earphone (no stereo option of course) on a long lead plugged directly into the TV headphone socket. A TV was chosen which has two separate audio channels to enable myself to hear using a single earphone and others directly through the TV speakers both with their own volume controls.

In October 2011 I attended a one week residential course at the Hearing Link Centre in Eastbourne tailored especially for those with NF2. If you ever have the opportunity to attend this course do so because it is very informative and helpful. A member of your family is allowed to go with you. I enjoyed the experience.

No other member of my family or relatives have NF2, including my son and daughter, for which I am very relieved.

For the future I believe the answer to our problems will come from drug therapies. It seems Avastin is already helping a number of NF2 patients and trust I may be a suitable candidate in a hope of not getting gradually worse. Thank goodness there are now at long last centrally organised, coordinated and funded NF2 clinics.

Best wishes to you and your family, medical experts and others who help, encourage and support us with NF2. Good luck and keep your chin up.

12. Fred Suter

Fred Suter was diagnosed with NF2 at the age of 17, he is now 26 years of age. Fred originates from Germany but lives in the UK during term times studying for a degree in Language and Linguistics. Being entirely deaf is no excuse in the eyes of Fred and he followed his dream despite the obvious challenge.

His story presents a journey from misery to happiness through the vital key of acceptance and illustrates how many things can be learned along the way. Fred affirms that nothing can be done about yesterday, and so today is the right day to love, believe, do, and mostly live.

The choice which wasn't any

If I mourned, what would it help? There's no other option, but to take it the way it comes and try to make the best out of it. At the beginning this may be the hardest part, but only through acceptance can you take the next steps. And who knows? You may even begin to enjoy that path.

What I learned is that after the initial sudden blow, which indeed can be hugely tough, it only gets better, if you want it to. Allow yourself some time. One big loss of time for me was when I started to ignore NF2, some years after diagnosis, because I just wanted to live. But as a young person, I now know that's not a wise thing to do with NF2. The future is still out there, for many years, so I need to be responsible for myself and my NF2 career, so that I can make the best decisions.

You only have one life and you live in the moment. So why grieve for what's gone or be sad because you can't do this or that anymore? Another thing I realised: You cannot plan your life. This counts for us with NF2 just as it counts for anybody.

NF2 is so different in every individual though and many will have different perceptions and experiences, but this is how I experienced it after becoming deaf.

But first things first, I'd like to tell you how it began in 2003: My story starts pretty 'normal': I was 17 years old, just successfully passed my exams in a secondary school. I had friends, hobbies; everything was just going normally, like it does in the average teenager's life. My holiday in the summer vacation was very nice too. Our neighbour noticed that my hearing wasn't quite right. I realised myself, but we all thought it was wax in my ears and didn't take it seriously. But it didn't go away, so I went to the doctor's. Result: No wax, no nothing. He sent me to for a CT scan. Result: Two small tumours in my head. After that they did an even more exact so called MRI, then I got the confirmation: A tumour on each side's nerve of hearing (acoustic nerve), one in the head's centre, and many more inside the body. They told me about a rare condition called Neurofibromatosis Type 2. Never had heard of it, never mind…Ok, right… I've always had such weird things all over my skin, but inside? And even in the head? Well, I felt a bit weird after that news; two weeks later I would have to go and have an operation.

Lots of misery followed in the years after, especially after my second surgery. But I know now that body and soul are interconnected; if I felt down, it was probably because of some health problems. However long those times were (e.g. two years of rehabilitation after second surgery), I always kept my true spirit, just maybe not as accessible in those times. But that's not me and it never will be. I'm too young for bitterness.

Back then, I would say I was pulled out of life. Who I thought to be friends, moved away from me, except very few close ones. I lost the grip of the world I belonged to and with it my identity until only my family was left. However, now, almost ten years into living with NF2 I'd say this condition gave me life, made it meaningful. For that I am kind of thankful and I now enjoy living life wherever I can.

At first, after the first surgery I was hard of hearing to a high degree. This stayed stable for five years and after the second one in 2008 I am now fully deaf, and since then live in complete silence. What proved at first an enormous strike in life, I have now found ways to cope with it.

The first step was acceptance of this fate. Not that I have swept it aside, rather that I have found ways of lessening the pain which deafness brings. At first there was the language part. I think if you want to enjoy your time with somebody else, you need a shared language to achieve this. For me and my family this meant learning sign language and over time I taught this to my closest friends so that they could find a way back to my real self, and still do that today. And boy, am I thankful for what having to learn sign language has given me.

At first, in terms of language, I must say it's a beautiful language, a way to express yourself. Then there is the deaf community. While it's a culture of its own, it is a community of holding together which many people dream of. And I could be part of it now, in a way. Although I'm not an early deaf person, with every year that passes I feel more and more comfortable in that world. Sign Language has ever since I went fully deaf become an integral part of my life and identity. I couldn't imagine living without the language anymore and I make sure Sign Language is spoken around me, even if only basic by hearing friends and family. At uni I have even founded a Sign Language society which is quite popular.

In public I find myself being avoided, it is almost impossible to meet new people. Many are so struck with helplessness when they face a communicative challenge, that they rather turn away or say nothing which seems the easiest solution for them. When I take that thought further, I realise it's not me directly, but rather communication with me which they avoid. So, I keep telling myself it is their loss, I like myself. Of course though, it is mine, too. Due to the failing small-talk and the normal gossip going around (who thought this would be important?) I feel shut out from personalities, from information, from other humans in general. But getting angry towards the many who seek to evade the situation is just a waste of energy. No doubt it's frustrating and disappointing though and it has become the norm.

I feel like I have to work hard and get to know many people, because there might just be someone who will not follow this general pattern. After all, I have interesting things to tell. So, actually it is an on-going fight about re-integrating myself back into society, or maybe it is just a straw of my past and true identity which I do not want let go.

There is of course the very convenient option to retreat into the online world. But I have agreed with myself that this is not the way, it makes me lonely ironically. I rather try it on the battlefield, which can be very frustrating; it is really hard to keep your spirits up if the society's behaviour just pulls them down again. But staying there, in the world I come from and in which I feel at home most, gives me some confidence in it and that way I don't lose the connection to it.

Of course me and my family all felt completely lost when we suddenly had to communicate by pen and paper after the first surgery. But after a few years we all began to understand the real meaning of the saying 'time heals all wounds'. NF2 has really redefined true family love within mine, and in some way or another I am even grateful for this fate. It enabled me to meet many nice people; to have new experiences; to learn what life is worth and to talk about things which actually matter. It enabled me to discover the strengths and potential in family and friends and myself, of which I was never aware. I had one of the best childhoods you could wish for, and that can never be taken away. I have taken Gandhi's words as my new motto: 'Don't cry because it's over. Smile because it happened.'

I am a language student at Southampton University, which has, having grown up in Germany, always been my dream (before becoming deaf). I thought to myself 'why should the deafness stop me?', so I just continued with it and it works well. Having me as a student means extra work for the tutors and others and of course for myself. But I'm up for it, and some great support is available; all you have to do is say what you need and ask for it, sometimes even fight for it.

I have this remote captioning service in my lectures, so that's just like the subtitles you can see in live TV shows and it makes me feel like I am at the same level as other students, despite my disadvantage.

Generally I enjoy challenges and that's what keeps me going. I see NF2 not as a disability itself (the feeling of being disadvantaged is created by society) but as a challenge, and I won't give up before it is resolved. Not only medicine, but technology has lots in store for us and I see a bright future.

Many people complain about not knowing what to do with their lives, having no essence in it. For me NF2 is a sense of life. It is certainly not boring and made me what I am today. Many people are just not very aware of the value of life and an advantage I have and they never will; being in this situation makes me realise it.

In Shantaram, the best book I have ever read, a quote goes "If you can't do anything about something, you have to accept that things could be worse and that you are completely helpless in the face of it" and I could write a whole book about all this, but Voltaire said "the longer we dwell on misfortunes, the greater is their power to harm us". So I will come to an end now.

So long…hang in there folks!

13. Gabriela Bazan

Gabriela Bazan originates from Peru and now lives in Chicago, USA. After obtaining her degree and moving to America, Gabriela began to attend classes in English and Business in order to maximise her opportunities. Gabriela also tells us how her passion for dancing will not be limited by her NF2 related challenges.

Gabriela Bazan was born in Lima, Peru, and was diagnosed with Neurofibromatosis Type 2 (NF2) when she was attending a university in 2004. Gabriela has had five brain surgeries and ten eye surgeries from 2004 to the present, which took place in Peru, Brazil, and the United States.

After her first surgery she developed vision, hearing and balance issues, and loss of facial nerve function; however, she went back to the university to culminate her studies and received her Bachelor's degree.

Over the next several years, she moved to the U.S. to start her new life. Thus, despite her gradual loss of hearing, she has been taking English and Business Classes in order to work and live comfortably in a country with a language and culture which is significantly different than her home country.

Combining activities of daily living with health treatments, she gets breaks to spend time dancing to Latino music and belly dancing. She loves dancing and says, "Music runs in my veins and in my feet. My bad balance cannot stop my passion for dancing. My feet move of their own free will. Every time I'm going to fall, my feet invent a new step, and I continue dancing."

14. Halina M.X.

Halina M.X. is 31 years of age and originated from Poland, but is now a resident of the UK. Halina and her older sister inherited NF2 from their mother, who was unaware of the condition in her lifetime.

When their mother very sadly passed away in 2011 the sisters were diagnosed with NF2. In her story Halina gives an insight into the recent years of her life living with NF2. She also talks about her travels overseas and passion for living life to the full.

Hi, my name is Halina, I am 31 years old. I am from Poland but have lived in the UK since 2004. I was diagnosed with NF2 in 2011 after taking a genetic test. I inherited NF2 from my mother. My older sister Irena also has NF2. My mother had a normal life, some problems with balance and hearing, but her condition did not affect her until age 61. She had a stroke when she was 64 years old and passed away in September 2011 without knowing she had NF2.

On 19th December 2011 I had an operation to remove a large tumour from the acoustic nerve on my left side. The operation was successful and the surgeons managed to remove the entire tumour without causing damage to my facial nerve. As a result from the surgery I became profoundly deaf in my left ear, but I was fitted with an Auditory Brainstem Implant (ABI). In May 2012 my processor was switched on and I have now started to learn to listen again with the ABI.

Just before my ABI was switched on the hearing on my right side started to deteriorate very fast and one day I woke up profoundly deaf on my right side. The surgeons and I are currently discussing what to do with the tumour on my right side, hopefully it will be possible to insert a cochlear implant which could help me to hear better than I can now.

I have lived with this condition for two years now. Me and my sister Irena support each other and I am a very lucky to have a loving and supportive husband also. After I was diagnosed with NF2 I wanted to make sure that I enjoyed life as much as I could until the time came for an operation.

My husband and I decided to cross Europe in the car. We drove from the UK and visited many countries including France, Holland, Belgium, Germany, Austria, Slovenia, Croatia, Bosnia-Herzegovina, Montenegro, Albania and Kosovo. Vienna in Austria was particularly beautiful, but my favourite place was Zagreb in Croatia. It was very interesting to experience all of the different cultures and to see all of these beautiful places.

My journey with NF2 has just begun.

15. Jan McGovern

Jan McGovern is 64 years of age and is from Suffolk, UK. Jan was diagnosed with the mosaic form of NF2 in early 2011 at the age of 62.

In her story Jan provides a deep insight into her journey with NF2 so far, from the emotions and reactions of the initial diagnosis through to how her life has now adapted to the challenges and changes that NF2 has brought.

Jan has taken a practical approach towards dealing with the condition and has kept her fighting spirit through the thick of it.

In 2000 I was a single mother with my oldest son having children and my youngest son still at home. I was employed full time as an Estate Agent Manager with a large Corporate Company; I was participating in aerobic classes, circuit training, the gym, swimming, and singing with a Choral Society.

Everything changed in 2001. The good - my son went to University, my daughter had her first child, and I met my husband. The bad - after a bout of what appeared to be an influenza type virus I became ill with what was formally diagnosed in 2004 as ME, which I discovered was far from being "yuppy flu" and was extremely debilitating.

My initial re-action was "fight it". I wasn't going to be beaten. However, my consultant told me "it will beat you every time, learn to respect it, or you'll end up useless, in a wheelchair". Reluctantly, I had to accept a change in my career. My exercise and singing ceased. I tried to not "boom and bust", something I still find hard to cope with. On a good day I want to take on the world, only to then drop the next few days.

With no immune system, was it an opening for NF2 to develop? I will never know.

I married in 2002. My husband's employment took him away from home during the week. Weekends we spent enjoying our love of music and the theatre or with family. The demands of my work, and the constraints of my illness, forced me to give up in November 2007, with much adjustment to early retirement.

In June 2010 I was experiencing pain in my right ear and found myself constantly at the doctors being treated for ear infections. By the end of the July I started to get tinnitus. This coincided with a visit to the opticians also offering free hearing tests. It showed a loss. My doctor referred me to the local hospital. It was decided I should have an MRI scan "as a precaution". I was not unduly concerned when asked to return for a second MRI scan, I was told it was normal procedure.

I was completely unprepared for the results. I'd gone on my own; my mind hadn't considered anything dramatic. I was bluntly told, "You have a tumour on your right acoustic nerve. We don't have the expertise, and are referring you to a specialist hospital". I don't think it had really registered, I just thought – an operation, take it out, job over. I vaguely remember I must have portrayed this as he said to me, quite forthrightly, "you do realise how serious this is don't you, it means drilling a hole in your skull" – I know, I went into shock. I have no recollection of leaving his office, but just remember finding the nearest loo and breaking down. It was a bad dream. I phoned my husband, he must have wondered what had hit him, my blubbering like a baby. I then had the drive home to an empty house.

The wait for the hospital appointment wasn't helped with the constant pain I was experiencing and tinnitus. I saw the consultant in January 2011, and was told he had seen what he thought was a tumour on the other ear which would indicate something called NF2, but he wanted more MRI scans, as much to disregard as to confirm the diagnosis. I think my brain just wanted to ignore everything as if it hadn't happened. The next few weeks I went into a memory stance where nothing sunk in. I had asked for some literature, but it didn't really register. I just kept holding onto his statement of being 'as much to disregard' as anything else.

I don't think anything prepares you for the final realisation that you have NF2. Unfortunately, the circumstance of finding out the final diagnosis wasn't quite straightforward, making it harder.

I don't think it registered with my family and it was hard for my friends. I had been ill for a while with ME; there was nothing to see with my NF2. It was just a case of 'mum having something more'. My husband kept his own thoughts to himself. The only thing he was adamant on was I was not going to have any operation.

Only my youngest son made the decision to be tested. He is getting married in 2013 and they want to start a family. Fortunately his test results came back negative, though he is to continue to be monitored for another three years. His brother's view was if he'd got NF2, then nothing he could do would change it. I'd only beat myself up with guilt if it was confirmed, so he'd rather not know. My daughter doesn't accept that I have NF2.

I was trying to take it all in whilst dealing with the pain. My GP is brilliant, what he doesn't know he always researches, and he tried various medications, which unfortunately my body rejected. I found it harder to get an understanding by the consultant.

I suppose I reached a plateau and the stoical part of me kicked in. I decided to find out as much as I could. I didn't have access to the internet, but used the literature from the hospital and contacted the Neuro Foundation. In turn the charity sent me a copy of their magazine with details of membership, and from this I contacted Hearing Link.

I enquired through my local authority and was put in touch with the sensory team who came to assess my needs and supplied me with equipment. My assessor is also deaf and she made me aware of a local lip reading class which I joined. The members of this class have all become firm friends. We meet when there are no classes.

My hearing loss continued. I was fitted with a hearing aid which was useful for a short time. I now have no hearing in my right ear. I am participating in a Vestibular Rehabilitation Programme to aid my balance - teach an old brain new tricks. I've used a mobility aid for a while; it has a seat which is useful.

I have continued to enjoy the theatre, ballet, opera with subtitles, and cinema, even though I don't catch all of the words spoken or the music sung. The tinnitus is always greater as soon as sound systems are switched on, but my love is so great, I will endeavour to continue. I also love reading.

In September 2011 I was invited with my husband to attend a Hearing Link course in Eastbourne. For the first time, it brought home to me just how destructive NF2 can be. With it came the realisation that I was lucky it hadn't appeared in my teens or twenties which I learnt was more the norm. It also showed what sheer determination can do to overcome the difficulties NF2 can cause; I have great admiration for those people. The week was very intensive, and I now believe it was too soon after my diagnosis for me to have got the full benefit of what was on offer. I much regret this. I would love the opportunity to be able to attend again.

As the year progressed, the pain and discomfort I was experiencing did not let up. I was getting screaming corkscrews of pain through the core of my ear. I felt as if I'd been punched in my right cheek and my chin and all through the top of my head more sharp pain. Nothing seemed to touch it – the only relief I seemed to get was to shut myself away without sound when there would be a bit of calm and I was so tired.

To the outside world I appeared and still do to be coping well – maybe that's my downfall – is that what we all do as a coping mechanism? Would it be better to "give in" and be "looked after"? I don't know. I feel very isolated at times despite having wonderful support. I am learning to use the services available and to be more open with my specialist NF2 nurse. I have a good blubber, then pick myself up and tell myself to deal with it!

I investigated possibilities. In the October I saw a consultant, and in the December had Gamma Knife Radio Stereotactic surgery. For me it wasn't straightforward, I reacted to the steroids given and there were complications after. I won't know until my next scan in March 2013 whether there is a change to the tumour – I'll reserve judgement until then!

The pain continues to be a problem – there are days when I just want to get a knife and cut out this alien in my head!

In October 2012 I was a day patient at the local hospital and had treatment which involved pulsed radio frequency along the occipital nerve to block nerve pain. I was told everything would be exacerbated until December when I should gain relief and after a taxing few weeks this proved to be the case. What a relief to be without so much pain and to feel human again!

I have recently attended an NF2 Patient Carer Day and it was brilliant. Work commitments made it impossible for my husband to be there. I'm sure it would have helped him, though he doesn't say. I feel for him, as he has to be my rock, so he must feel isolated too.

After much nagging from friends and family I have entered the 21st century and have become connected to broadband – why didn't I do it before I ask myself - it's very addictive!

I'm now looking at what is on offer to assist one sided hearing – that's my next venture.

Having NF2 isn't great, but it has brought me in contact with so many different people. I have made a lot of new friends that I wouldn't have done. It does have its positives. I have no intention of being the little old lady stuck in the corner, and the battle will continue!

16. Jessica Stone

Jessica Stone was diagnosed with NF2 at the age of 15, despite there being signs of the condition earlier on in life. Jessica is now 27 years of age and lives in Michigan, USA. Jessica takes us on a wonderful and inspiring creative journey by comparing her NF2 related challenges to life on the beach.

Jessica's story shows us that so much can be learned about life through having NF2. That there is so much to discover about ourselves, and so much to marvel in outside of our shells; if only we have the eyes to see it, the heart to love it, and the hand to gather it to ourselves. Life itself, is a miracle.

My name is Jessica Stone, I'm 27 years old and I live in Michigan.

I learned to swim at the age of 3. My parents could only do so much to teach me how to swim; kicking my feet to keep my head above water was up to me. Some of my earliest memories are of my family spending the day at the beach. I can almost feel the soft sand under my feet and the taste of ice cream on my tongue. When I close my eyes I see the sailboats passing by while we splash in Lake Michigan. My favorite memory is building sand castles with my brother & sister on the lakeshore only to watch the waves sweep it all away. NF2 is a Beach.

There isn't a blue print to building a sand castle, or a blue print to NF2. I started having surgery at age 7. My brother played sports, my sister could sing, and surgery every couple of months was my thing. No I joke, art was my thing. Surgery was just something I did, not something I dwelled on. My family never treated me differently. My childhood was pretty awesome. It became routine to get Chinese food the night before surgery, bring my stuffed bunny to surgery, and take a ride by the lake during my recovery. Although the waves couldn't wash away the pain, the sound of them crashing on the shore was relaxing.

When a storm rolls in over the lake the rip current is so strong that the waves will knock you over and the next thing you know you're underwater. If you don't fight it you'll drown. Being diagnosed with NF2 at 15 was a series of waves that continued to knock me down. Within months of being diagnosed I was having surgery to remove an acoustic neuroma leaving me deaf in my left ear. A few months after that was an invasive surgery on my spine. Being half deaf and in a neck brace was an adjustment; being diagnosed was crushing. It made my already close relationship with my family stronger. Everything happened so fast that I never got a chance to catch my breath. My classmates wrote me off as "Cancer Girl"; my Biology teacher was fascinated with my health; my surgeon pushed for me to learn Sign Language. With all the pressure I just wanted my orange arm floaties to help me swim.

A ship in the harbor is safe, but that is not what ships are built for. After a few minor outpatient procedures and awesome spring breaks with my sister I graduated high school. I chose to take a break in my education to travel in between surgeries. Over the past ten years I have hiked National Parks all over the United States; climbed the Great Wall of China while spending a summer teaching English; been blessed to dip my toes in both the Atlantic and Pacific Ocean; even Whale watched in Canada. Through all my travels, there is no harbor like the one at home.

It's always more enjoyable to take the trolley to the beach with someone than going alone. My mom has been to every surgery and doctors appointment of mine. She's probably racked up more mileage on her Jeep from carting me around than attending all my brother's football games. My mom isn't just my chauffeur; she's my voice of reason when things are over my head. I was dropped from my parents insurance at 19. I guess the insurance people thought my NF would magically disappear... no such luck. I had throat surgery scheduled a few months after being dropped. Right away my mom was on the phone with the hospital and made it possible to still do surgery (even get me back on insurance). The surgery was a success, but paralyzed a vocal cord making me sound like a squeaky seagull.

Birds of a feather flock together. Watching birds fly off into the horizon at sunset is inspiring. Now if we want to fly we have to give up the stuff that weighs us down. My circle of friends has always been small, self-absorbed, and indifferent of me having NF2. Reaching out to the NF2 community after high school made me feel not alone in the world. We are all chasing after a cure; we're never going to give up on that. I met my best friend on a beach in Florida. NF2 brought us together, but it was fate that we'd be friends. We can sit on the beach together say nothing about NF2 but we have each other to lean on when times are dreary.

When dark clouds roll in, right before the rain falls there is this eerie silence that spreads across the whole beach. Becoming completely deaf was a storm cloud that has loomed over my head for eight years. Spring of 2008 I decided to give up my hearing to save my life. There never is enough time to store all the sounds you want to remember into your memory bank. There is never enough time to say all that you wanted to say. As fast as lightening my hearing was gone. One minute I'm being rolled into the operating room with headphones on listening to music, then I'm waking up in the ICU (Intensive Care Unit) to a sea of faces but no words are coming out of their mouths. There was this dizzying loud static noise in my ears and I started to panic. Then my sister signed to me "how are you feeling?" and my mom was trying to tell me not to cry but signed "don't rain" and I burst into giggles. That's how I knew everything was going to be all right.

The funny thing about weather in Michigan is that it changes all the time. Just when you think it's going to rain all day the clouds clear and you're off to the beach to soak up some sun. By the grace of God, my surgeon saved a single sound wave making me a candidate for a Cochlear Implant. My Cochlear Implant was activated in the Fall of 2008 and I was able to hear my parents say "I love you" and the waves crashing on the beach. That winter my mom and I swam to Milwaukee (68 miles) in the pool. Best of all, I became an aunt!!

Learning to hear with my Cochlear Implant is essentially like teaching my nephew to build a sandcastle for the first time. As simple as it sounds, it takes patience to show him to shovel sand into the bucket, flip it over, and repeat. With the CI it took dedication to connect sounds to my environment. I have been known to pop three bags of popcorn in one night just to hear them pop. I pretty sure I've watched Batman: The Dark Knight at least twenty-five times to figure out the difference between talking and sound effects. I could have a conversation without people repeating themselves. I'll admit it was a love-hate relationship at first, but I was making so much progress. But I guess all good things come to an end eventually.

Unlike the wave that knocked over my nephew's sandcastle, my wave was completely unpredicted. I was falling asleep all the time and then one day my Cochlear Implant just stopped. The MRI showed both acoustic neuromas grew back and excess brain fluid was trapped in my skull. All the progress I made was washed away like a sandcastle. Fortunately even before I could pick my jaw up off the floor my surgeon had a plan, shunt surgery and chemotherapy. It was like being diagnosed all over again; I had mixed emotions and disbelief. I had my fingers crossed hoping it was someone else's scan; I started Avastin in the Spring of 2010 till recently when I needed a break. The waves at the beach are silent now, but I still hear them in my heart. I'm rather unsure of what my future holds, but I can only hope for a cure for upcoming generations because NF2 IS A BEACH!!!

17. Joanne Page

Joanne Page is 49 years of age and from Worcestershire, UK. She was diagnosed with NF2 at the age of 26 and although she has been through numerous NF2 related surgeries she still manages to enjoy the good life in between times.

Joanne talks about making the absolute most of her current situation and also shows us that, sometimes, good things fall apart so that better things can fall together.

I was diagnosed with NF2 when I was 26 years old, I am now 49. To date I have had more than thirty operations as a result of NF2.

I live with permanent pain which is kept at a level I can cope with and I avoid doing anything to aggravate the pain as it then becomes unbearable. I have physical problems including facial paralysis, blurred and double vision, I'm profoundly deaf, have severe weakness, balance problems and foot drop in my right foot.

As soon as I left school I got a job and really enjoyed working for the company. I was very happy there but after my first operation I was only able to continue working part-time. Unfortunately even this proved to be more than I could cope with so I had to stop working.

In 2009 I had my second acoustic neuroma removed and had an Auditory Brainstem Implant fitted (ABI) to help me with lip reading and it really is very useful to me. Even though lip reading is incredibly difficult it would be so much harder without the aid of the implant.

Being the only person in my family with NF2 it was life-changing when I was diagnosed and obviously this had an effect on many people.

I had been married for only four years when I was diagnosed with NF2 and a few years later my husband decided he no longer wanted his life affected by NF2 and he walked away. I am no longer able to drive - and this is one thing I really miss! I also made the heart breaking decision not to have children. I love babies and it was part of my plan to have a family.

I joined a lip-reading group nearly ten years ago and we meet every Thursday morning. The group is made up of people from all walks of life, men and women, young and old, all very different but we all have a hearing loss. We all benefit so much from our different experiences. The challenges we have due to hearing loss brings us together weekly with our tutor who also has a hearing loss. This has helped to create such good bonds and friendships that are very valuable and meaningful. I met my fiancé at this group and we've been together since 2005. I've never been happier than I am now. I never thought I would meet any one else let alone someone who would want to spend the rest of his life with me!

I am very fortunate to be part of a very supportive, understanding and loving family who I appreciate immensely. My fiancé has recently become my registered carer and he is continually on the lookout for me and understands me very well. Without him and his desire (he says it's a pleasure) to be there for me and to not let things be a setback, I wouldn't be able to enjoy life the way that I do. Yes there are tears, but also a lot of laughter.

In January 2012 I had an operation to remove four neurofibromas from my right leg and unfortunately I now have foot drop which if you knew me and my love of high heeled shoes you would know how much it upset me not being able to wear them anymore because I now have to wear a splint. At first the thought of having to wear flat shoes was a very real issue for me but I can't believe the fun I have had choosing flat shoes, a whole new wardrobe full, wow!! And believe it or not I love wearing them more than my heels so it wasn't the end of the world.

Despite my difficulties with NF2 I am very happy and content with my life. I get enormous pleasure from the most simple of things and really don't yearn or long for things to be any different. My day to day life suits me and enables me to cope with and enjoy living. One thing that I never say is that I wish I had a normal life, there's no such thing, because what is normal for one is not for another. This is my normal life!

Just after I was diagnosed with NF2 I was listening to the radio (yes I did once have hearing) and it was an interview with Marti Caine, a comedienne. She had just been diagnosed with cancer and the interviewer asked if she ever asked "why me?" and her response was "why not me". That really had an effect on me and I can identify with it very much.

I have a very encouraging saying on my memo board in the kitchen: "Don't wait for the storm to pass, learn to dance in the rain".

I am very grateful for the on-going support from all sources that I receive and the many ways that people have sought to help me and enhance my life.

I realized very early on that it was better and easier for me to accept that I have NF2 and the way it has changed my life rather than hope each day that it might just go away. My life might not necessarily have gone according to plan due to having NF2 - so I've just changed the plans!

18. Joanne Ward

Joanne Ward is 42 years of age and from Nottingham, UK. Joanne was diagnosed with NF2 at 29 years of age and in her story focuses on life after the initial surgical impacts of NF2, as so she states: there is life after it.

Joanne explains that sometimes life does go on a detour, but she shows that it is possible to get life back on track, even though it can be difficult. Often, we learn more through the journey, and in her story Joanne demonstrates that happiness is not a destination, it's a way of life.

This is my story about life after NF2 - because there is life after it.

Life before it was good and normal, as I didn't know I even had NF2 until I was 29 years old. I have been living with NF2 for thirteen years now and I am the first in my family to have the condition.

I still remember the day like it was yesterday; that was the day I was "told", that I saw the scans with the big white patches on it. They explained about the tumours and told me they had a "slot" in five days if I wanted it (for the removal that is). So that's how it all started for me, because up until that point life was normal - I was a normal school kid, adolescent and adult. I did normal things, went on normal holidays, joined in with the normal things you did as a kid, teenager or 20-something.

After that bit, life seemed to go on hold for about five months, and I wanted to know at the time, why no-one else's life stood still like mine did.

With the love and support of family and friends, and especially my husband (who has been my rock throughout and our relationship has not faltered in any way), I have finally got my life back on track. I returned to work, travelled (some of) the world, and have done things I never thought I would have done living with NF2.

Life changed at first and was an endless round of going to see physiotherapists, speech therapists, consultants etc. I wanted some kind of label on my back so that people would know what I'd been through - or a label telling them that I was deaf. I really didn't want anyone talking to me at all and my confidence took a dive! It was difficult to embrace the changes at times. I immediately went deaf in my right ear, and was unable to wear my contact lenses after fourteen years due to my dry eye. I was also slowly losing the hearing on my left side. So it was also a time about planning for the future, of what, or would, might happen.

So after three months I returned to work part-time and started with lip-reading classes, which I found really useful. I am not the world's greatest lip-reader and I never shall be but it gets you up and about and meeting people, talking to people, and sharing your experiences. I also had a facial palsy so it was also about being accepted for how I looked. The group was small so I was able to get to know them and they all had hearing problems so I didn't feel like it was just me.

Then came sign language classes - again supported by my husband. We both went along to learn sign language which was actually quite fun and that's where I met more new people who I would credit with giving me another part of my life back by getting me involved socially and taking me out (even without husband!). It's these people who gave me back some of my independence to do things I wouldn't have normally done without their gentle coaxing. Before that, I didn't go out, not socially anyway, and it changed the way I liked to socialise, preferring to be with close friends or family for a quite meal out - not that I was one for clubbing anyway!

In between all of this we enjoyed holidays to far flung places of the world. Although I couldn't always communicate by hearing what people said, seeing and embracing another's culture became fun. I would, and still do, rely heavily on my husband whenever we go abroad or holiday anywhere, and on planes etc. Even now, I am not too sure if I could actually do that one on my own. In fact, having my facial palsy, I have found that my face is probably more memorable. Holidaying in Thailand, three years apart, I had a waiter ask me if I'd visited about three years earlier... And I had, he'd recalled me because of my face! I'm not sure still to this day if that was good or bad!! But sometimes you don't want to be the memorable face; you want to be the one that can disappear into the crowd, but you can't.

The hearing on my left side gradually deteriorated to a point where I am now completely deaf. The hearing aids were of no use but with the lip-reading and sign language, I manage to get by. Sometimes by putting two and two together (and coming up with 5!). I don't feel that I let my deafness or lack of balance dictate who I am, but I am probably more choosy about things that I do, within the realms of knowing my limitations (unless I am pushed to do things otherwise!).

I gave up work after a few years to care for our first-born son, D. It was the next challenge I needed (and wanted). It was daunting knowing that I would have to look after a child when I was deaf but I had the great support of family, friends, neighbours and social services (who supplied me with a few helpful gadgets like a vibrating baby monitor). When D was about 6 months old we then started venturing out more and went to baby sign class and other baby classes, then onto toddlers' group and pre-school and eventually school.

Having D, as I say, gave me a new challenge and it is continuing to do so. I feel children get you doing all sorts of things you don't normally do or want to do and it's taken me out of my comfort zone which has been fantastic for me. I have met many people and done many things I never would have done if he hadn't come along. So he has been great for my self-esteem.

I taught D to sign to me so we can communicate and I can read his lips, we don't always put two and two together but we work at it until we understand each other. Although he knows mummy cannot hear him and will sign to me, I am not sure he completely understands what being deaf means.

His brother, O, came along a few years later, giving me another set of challenges. I am currently trying to teach him to sign also and I am very sure the pair of them will set me new challenges throughout their life.

Having the children gave me new things to focus on. Although I have the problems with deafness, some facial paralysis, and a lack of balance, I try not to let them detract me from everyday life. Friends and family do know I am deaf, as do a few people I meet daily (e.g. on the school run/D's teachers), but I don't go out of my way to inform people if it is not necessary.

I am now at the point in life where although I am settled living with NF2, I am about to embark on a whole new set of challenges and changes. I will shortly be having facial rehabilitation surgery which I am really looking forward to and also having tests in the New Year for a cochlear implant. So there will be exciting and changing times ahead for me. I am also looking forward very much to the children growing up, doing well in school and seeing what they make of their lives. The holidays will no doubt continue and even with my unbalanced balance I shall be trying my hand at skiing next year!!!

Medically, I have annual MRI scans, which don't really bother me too much, I am just glad they are keeping an eye on me! After that I usually have a follow-up with the (now) NF2 team. Before that it was just the ENT surgeon or neurosurgeon, again that doesn't really bother me as I feel that I would "know" if there was anything untoward to worry about. They usually check my hearing first, but the last few times haven't bothered as they know now that I cannot hear anything. I have recently seen the Genetics Counsellor with the children so that they are "in the system" and can be seen when necessary. It does worry me about passing NF2 onto the children, but there are great medical advances being made all the time and I would hope that if they do have NF2 it wouldn't stop them doing anything they wanted to do. I hope they'd have an easier time of things than what I did and that they don't hold it against me for having them in the first instance.

I only actually know of one other person who has NF2 and that was only because of my curiosity to know how other people lived and coped, and whether they had children or not. Our communication was only recent (2-3 years ago) though and before that I did have some contact with the BANA charity. The charity gave me all sorts of useful information and I attended a couple of their meetings when they were local to where I live as I don't really like driving too far now and especially in the dark! I feel that knowing at least one other, and others at a distant through the NF newsletters etc. makes me happier knowing that I am not alone and at least someone else has experienced the things that I have.

I only knew of one other person that was deaf before I was, but they don't use sign-language or anything and live a complete and full life. Since going deaf I have met a few other deaf (or deafened) people and find that each person is different in the way they deal with it. I find some people want to be fully integrated/involved with the deaf community and others (as I would class myself), don't. I feel that whatever you choose to do then as long as it makes you happy, there are no right or wrong answers.

19. Joe Guglielmi

This story is a beautiful tribute to the late Joe Guglielmi (1985–2012) written by his brother Tom Guglielmi and his mother Lynda McFaull.

Joe's passion to support others, even whilst dealing with his own struggles, is an admirable and selfless quality that we can all learn from. May the spirit of Joe Guglielmi continue to inspire and encourage through this everlasting testimony to a man, brother, son, friend and angel, who laughed and fought until the sun went down.

Joe was an inspiration to all around him, and brought joy into people's lives with his kindness, laughter and passion for living life to the full. Joe faced the adversity of his life with Neurofibromatosis Type 2 with great courage and he was always incredibly positive and fun-loving, full of energy and love for his family and friends.

Despite being completely deaf for most of the last decade, Joe never came across as deaf to many people he met. He had an amazing ability to connect with people, whether on one of his many exciting holidays, down the pub watching football, or supporting other young people with NF2. Coupled with an extraordinary ability to lip-read meant many people didn't fully realise the extent of Joe's condition.

Joe always dealt with his symptoms with great courage and stubbornness – the multiple invasive surgeries, the never-ending hospital appointments, and countless times laid up in bed – all the time with mum by his side. Joe said several times that mum was his 'rock', and that as long as she was there he knew everything was going to be ok. He was SO brave – he took everything in his stride, and you knew that whatever was thrown at him, he'd come out fighting.

One side of Joe's face was paralysed as a result of his NF2. One of the effects of this is that he usually had to drink through a straw. Over time, the drink in question graduated from coke to Budweiser, onto Guinness and recently onto Champagne. Joe undoubtedly could have represented Britain for his ability to drain a can of Guinness through a straw. Another of Joe's passions was food; a Big Mac at McDonalds, a Simply Outrageous ice-cream sundae at Sloppy Joe's, one of dad's mixed grills, or one of mum's cooked breakfasts.

When Joe used to go to Italy as a child, our grandmother used to melt slabs of chocolate into a mug – which Joe would happily knock back for breakfast! And then there's the small matter of Steak. Joe loved his holidays to Goa; he's probably the only man I'll ever know that could go on a three-week Indian holiday and have steak for dinner on EVERY single one of the twenty-one nights. Dad introduced Joe to his first 32-ounce steak at Bella Pais in Colchester, not believing that he would ever finish it. How very wrong he was! This quickly became the traditional catch-up for Joe and dad, with many more huge steaks being demolished since then.

Technology played a big part in Joe's life, particularly after he was diagnosed with NF2. He loved playing on his Wii and Playstation 3 with his communicator guides. Facebook was also a big deal to Joe. With face-to-face communication sometimes being difficult, he loved chatting to people online, and would be genuinely thrilled when people took the time to chat to him.

Joe really enjoyed playing pool and tenpin bowling. Those who played against him will most likely recall that he had a highly flexible interpretation of the rules! Nobody could throw a bowling ball like Joe, have it bounce off the bumpers no fewer than ten times and then get a strike.

Another of Joe's passions was Manchester United, of whom he was a committed supporter until the end. Some of his favourite times in recent months were spent down at Yate's or Riley's watching matches.

Joe had the loudest, most infectious laugh – and he really loved to laugh. When sitting downstairs at home, we'd frequently hear roars of laughter come out of the blue - everyone would wonder what on earth he was watching. At the cinema - another of Joe's favourite activities - we'd be watching a subtitled performance, and invariably Joe would end up in convulsions of laughter - even at films that really weren't meant to be that funny! Some of his fellow spectators tended to sink in their seats; others thought it was great and just joined in.

Behind the laughter and the football banter, Joe was the most gentle, loving and caring man. He loved giving people cuddly toys as presents, and made sure to always send out a huge number of Christmas cards and postcards from his various holidays. He would always be there with open arms to give everyone he met the biggest bear hugs imaginable, and he absolutely hated seeing anyone upset or unhappy. He was very affectionate with all of his family - especially his mum, with whom he shared an extra close bond.

Joe has proved to be an inspiration through his work with the Neuro Foundation and Hearing Concern LINK. Over the years, he and his mum have actively supported young people and their families who had been newly-diagnosed with NF2. Many of those who Joe helped have said how he gave them hope, and how his courage and fighting spirit was a huge source of inspiration for their own futures. Last year, Joe and Mum were invited to a garden party at Buckingham Palace in recognition of their work. I'm not sure her Majesty has ever seen anyone demolish so many plates of cucumber sandwiches and cakes with so much enthusiasm as Joe before!

Kirstie, Joe's girlfriend, died tragically in a car accident back in 2009. It is a comforting thought for us, and for Kirstie's family, to know that Joe and Kirstie are together again in heaven. Kirstie could talk for England, and with Joe being completely deaf, many commented at the time that it was a match made in heaven.

We had nine amazing years with Joe since he was first diagnosed with NF2, living life to the full. It is ironic that Joe has left us at one of the happiest points in his life. But in many ways, Joe is still with us – watching over us and sending us a virtual hug when we need one. He lives on in our memories and stories, and in what we have become because of him. So when you log on to Facebook, when you see Manchester United in action, when you hear someone laughing hysterically in the cinema – remember Joe, and his affection, his huge bear hugs and his laughter. Remember how courageous and stubborn he was in the face of adversity. And remember how amazingly happy and content he was, and how much joy he brought to our own lives.

20. Julie Baker

Julie Baker lives in the tranquil countryside of Devon and was diagnosed with NF2 at 55 years of age. Julie talks about the difficult adjustments she has had to make in her life after being diagnosed, including an early retirement, but how these have led her to new opportunities.

My life has changed greatly since being diagnosed and having treatment for Neurofibromatosis Type 2, not for the worst and probably for the better. NF2 has made me realise that when one door closes another one opens with new opportunities.

I was diagnosed in 2010 when I was 55 years old after my family noticed (and mentioned frequently) that I was becoming slightly hard of hearing. I denied it, blamed my age and continued to have the television on loud and accused people of mumbling on the telephone. After a few months, rather half-heartedly, I went for a hearing test and discovered that my family were right and I had severe hearing loss in my left ear. There then followed rather quickly doctors visits, referral to local ENT department, MRI scans, various tests and finally a visit to the large regional hospital where I was given the diagnosis of NF2.

Suddenly I had an illness that I had never heard of, and which I had from virtually the moment I was conceived, and that I had no symptoms for (apart from a hearing loss). Specialists and consultants, professors and experts, support nurses and advisors were all waiting to tell me about my new situation.

I had three brain tumours that had been growing since I was in my thirties and two of them were of a size that meant they had to be removed within the next year. I had previously had excellent health and I worked full time as an assessment officer in Social Services. I had never had surgery, only been in hospital to have my children and I was very apprehensive about everything. The diagnosis of brain tumours is very frightening and although I carried on working for six weeks until my first operation, I found it hard to concentrate. My work colleagues made comments such as "I don't know how you keep so calm", "you are very brave", I didn't feel calm and I didn't feel very brave.

Both operations were successful in that the tumours were completely removed, but I was left with some physical difficulties. Nothing too major, but I have poor balance, limited right hand movement and no hearing in my left ear. The left side of my face is "stiff" which has completely changed my voice as I now have problems forming words and sound very posh and rather drunk! To the amusement of my extended family I now sound like my mother after a few Sherries.

I was not able to drive for a year after my surgery and as I am the only driver in the family that did cause some difficulties. I am very grateful to the friends who meant it when they offered to help and chauffeured me around. I am also thankful for the hospital car services whose volunteers were always cheerful and reassuring when they picked me up at ridiculously early hours to attend appointments. I also learnt the art of online shopping, really brilliant; you "click" on the items which are then delivered to your house!

The big shock came when I had been off work for almost a year (after a 35 year excellent health record) when I was visited at home by my manager and told that I was going to be dismissed on the grounds of ill health. I was given the highest ill health retirement which meant my lump sum and pension were released early and enhanced as if I had continued to work until I was 65 years old.

So totally unexpectedly I found myself retired at the age of 56 years old with no time to prepare for it.

My husband and I were living in rented accommodation in a seaside town where we had lived for 25 years. We decided with my lump sum - and some money left to me by my late parents - to buy a small house. We wanted to move to the country and saw (after several disasters) a lovely small house near to Dartmoor in a row of ten houses surrounded by beautiful countryside. Fortunately for us the property prices were falling, the people selling had already moved and accepted our offer, so we moved in almost straight away. Neither of us has regretted our decision and we are really enjoying our new life. Although my balance is poor I am able to enjoy wonderful six mile walks on the Tarka Trail that is only a short distance from our house. I also go for long walks on the North Devon coast. We now have a lovely garden and enjoy working there. I can mow the lawn using the mower for balance - my husband tells me its good exercise!

NF2 has changed my life in that I am now retired and have all the time I need to do the things I love and spend time with my husband and family. I value the time to do what I enjoy without feeling guilty when I indulge myself with a good book or do something that is just for me.

I am still adjusting to my limitations but I feel it is my perception of them more than other peoples that cause me problems. I had always been quite organised (or bossy) and sorted everything at home and it was hard to sit back and let others do it. The Christmas after my first operation I had to let the rest of the family organise the food, decorations etc. Of course they did it wonderfully and everything went well. My professional life had been arranging care/assistance for others and now I was on the receiving end of therapists and carers and I found it quite a difficult adjustment to make.

I am the first person in my family to have NF2 and like me, none of them had ever heard of it. My two children aged 27 and 30 are having tests to see if they have inherited it. I do hope they are clear but if they are not at least it will be found early and the treatment less radical than mine was.

I sometimes forget I cannot hear on the left and have to take great care crossing roads. I get a shock when I hear my voice because in my head I think my old voice is still there.

It is fairly early days in my NF2 journey and it is thought I have the mosaic form of the illness (i.e. not in all the cells) as it has only affected one side and I still have good hearing in my right ear. My family have been very supportive and encouraged me to do as much as I am able to. I am now doing some voluntary work and have joined a local group where I now live.

I hope this book helps people newly diagnosed with NF2 as the unknown is a scary place. My advice would be DON'T look it up on the internet but talk to the advisors and support workers who are always willing to help.

21. Julie Broome

Julie Broome has the mosaic form of NF2. In her story Julie explains how although she had no control over the progression of the condition, she did have control over the effect it would have on her life.

She talks about how she trained to become a teacher of the Deaf to enable her to continue working in the eventuality of her losing her hearing.

I have now known I've had NF2 for fifteen years, and although it has shaped the decisions I've made in my life, I don't think it has taken control and made those decisions for me.

The symptoms of my first vestibular schwannoma (VS) were in my mid-twenties. As a busy working single mum, slight hearing loss in my right ear wasn't much of a priority. However, over the next four years as the hearing became progressively worse, I visited my GPs on several occasions in search of an answer. Evidently a healthy young person with a one sided hearing loss wasn't much of a priority to them either and I wasn't referred to the hospital for further investigation.

Life moved on: I was now at university about to embark on the final semester of my degree when my parents kindly paid for a private consultation to work out why I could no longer hear out of my right ear. I had a battery of tests and as none could adequately explain my hearing loss I was sent for an MRI.

Maybe it was because I was young or because I was busy, but during this time I had no inkling it might be something serious. I felt perfectly well and was more concerned about being accepted on a teacher training course than I was about the MRI results. This meant that when the consultant told me I had a brain tumour, I was in disbelief. He told me he was going to refer me to the best ENT surgeon he knew but I would need an operation and then three months to recover. I thanked him for the advice but explained that I simply was too busy to have an operation now as I had a dissertation to complete and an application to make.

The best ENT surgeon he knew was one of the top NF2 surgeons in the country. I am so grateful that I was referred to a very safe pair of hands. I met him after a three hour drive followed by a three hour hospital wait. His office was a small crowded room full of medical students. I wasn't told I had NF2, and the medical students standing behind me were asked to diagnose me based on my scan (a very unusual presenting VS) and my age. As they all failed miserably in their pursuit he told them it would appear I had NF2. Initially, I thought that must be a good thing: at least they knew what it was so that they would be able to cure me.

The operation was in May, three whole months after being told about the tumour. I looked the same but nothing else was the same. In those months I planned for the worst. I did practical things like writing my will and sorting out my life insurance. I did important things: making memories with my daughter, having our photographs taken and buying and engraving a locket for her. I looked at different scenarios: if I did live but was disfigured would I be able to teach - the course tutors told me not. My then boyfriend told me if this happened we could move somewhere where no one knew him. It was hard for those around me but it was very hard for me too. At the end of the three months there were far fewer people around to support me. Those that were there were good and fifteen years on one is now my husband, and the other two are among my closest friends.

It took thirteen hours and twelve very clever surgeons to remove the tumour. They only nudged my facial nerve in the operation which left my face unaffected. The euphoria for being alive was matched only by my exhaustion, but I was determined to get stronger and carry on my life as planned. I completed my degree and four months later embarked on the teaching course.

Surviving the brain tumour had been my prime concern and I had focused little attention on NF2 as a whole. My doctors, however, had examined me thoroughly for the disease and had now also dissected and inspected the tumour. Weeks after the operation I received a long and detailed letter from the geneticist explaining how I had an oddly presenting tumour but it wasn't NF2. Now all I had to do was get strong and be thankful.

A year on whilst in my first teaching post, I went for my first annual scan results and was shocked to be told I had a large meningioma in the centre of my head. They diagnosed NF2. I explained that they were mistaken and I had it in writing that I had not got the disease, but pictures speak louder than words and the image on the scan was clear. I went home and in the next few hours I had a tremendous pain at the site of the tumour, and knowing it must have been psychosomatic didn't make it hurt any less.

As this tumour was new, this gave me time and a degree of control to find out about NF2 and to investigate treatment options. The Internet and access to information was much more difficult then and surgeons were reluctant to recommend alternative treatment for tumours that could be treated surgically.

Everything I read and was told about NF2 spoke about deafness and this seemed an inevitable part of the condition. Although I had no control over the progression of the disease, I did have control over the effect it would have on my life. Deafness didn't have to prevent me from teaching or isolate me. In 2000 I embarked on a 2 year part time MA to become a teacher for the deaf. The course was weekend and holiday based so meant I didn't have to stop working. I also started signing classes and read as much as I could about deafness.

Four years after the meningioma first appeared it had reached a stage where it could no longer live in my head without causing damage. Other meningiomas of varying sizes had now joined it and my surgeons were keen for them to be removed. I was still determined not to have further surgery and against their best advice they reluctantly referred me to have Radio-static surgery (RSS).

RSS is a procedure where focused beams are targeted on the tumour, cutting off the blood supply and preventing it from growing. To achieve this you are fitted with a frame to keep your head perfectly still and go into a device that looks like a MRI machine. However horrible having the frame fitted was it was far easier than recovering from surgery. The immense kindness of the radiographers made a huge difference. I had this procedure twice on different sets of tumours and both times the staff were amazing and I was back working in a particularly challenging school within a week.

Years went by with annual scans showing the surgery and RSS had both been successful and as I approached 40 I was beginning to think I may not grow any more tumours and I may remain hearing albeit only in one ear. I married my partner of ten years and we thought about having a child through IVF so any NF genes could be screened out. We were reassured by doctors that there was no evidence that a pregnancy would stimulate more tumour growth.

My next annual scan I went for the results on my own for the first time: such was my confidence that everything would be fine. Unfortunately a microscopic bud of a VS was found on my hearing side. I naively thought that as the tumour was so tiny a dose of RSS would be sufficient to stop it growing, but my doctor explained the results for this type of tumour were less positive and my best option was to simply wait until the tumour was becoming problematic then to consider options.

Although the consultant went to great pains to say it didn't mean I would inevitably become deaf, as far as I could see this was the only possible scenario. The only question was when. My rusty ten year old teacher of the Deaf qualification I would now need to use and my basic signing skills would need to be improved on. The idea of another child had been very much been quashed by this news. Almost a year from the scan I was studying for my BSL level 2 qualification and was working as a peripatetic teacher of the Deaf.

Time went by and the tumour grew and fortunately for me medical science also bounded forward. As neither conventional surgery nor RSS were likely to preserve my remaining hearing, and despite all the preparations I'd made for being deaf, I was still eager to avoid it. Drug trials were progressing and I took the latest research on the Sorafenib trail to my next annual appointment. I was surprised when I was met with the same response as I had had previously when I'd spoken to my surgeons about a different treatment years earlier, which was basically that drug treatments were potentially dangerous and no one yet knew of their long term effects. The first three annual scans showed minimal growth.

My last annual scan was just before Christmas 2011, I didn't get my results until Valentine's Day. Although the tumour did not need treatment it was no longer microscopic and it had grown considerably in that year. Feeling my hearing time was running out, I asked if either drug treatment or possibly a cochlear implant (CI) might give me some hope of hearing. Avastin treatment was now being offered and having some positive results. I was given the same mantra about drug treatments as before but referred to another hospital for a discussion on CIs.

The hospital did speech and pure tone hearing tests on my remaining ear. Although the pure tone detected only a mild loss, the speech test results showed my hearing had already become significantly affected by the tumour. The consultant agreed to try and find out if I had a cochlear nerve intact in my deaf ear that would be suitable for implantation but the chances were slim. He also told me about the amazing results they were having with Avastin.

The cochlear nerve when tested was dead, and the consultant couldn't give me any certainty that they'd be able to preserve the nerve in my remaining ear once the tumour was removed. So Avastin was my only hearing chance. Unfortunately, I didn't meet the strict criteria. I wrote to the hospital and visited my MP's surgery who also lobbied the hospital on my behalf. I went to the NF2 weekend in Sheffield and pleaded with specialists to let me have the drug and save my hearing.

At the end of this summer they made no promises but did review the scans in case the measurements obtained from the previous hospital were incorrect. They were. I had met the criteria all along. In September I had my first Avastin infusion and I have now had my fifth. In December I will find out if it has been successful in halting my tumour growth. The results from other patients have been so positive I am in no doubt it will also be successful for me.

I am fortunate to have the mosaic (milder) form of NF2 and although I have had four procedures to get rid of different tumours each one of these has been successful. The most stressful part of the condition for me is the arrival of new tumours and then the point where they need to be dealt with. In between these times I am able to live my life very normally. Normality in itself is something important to strive for. I have an amazing family, and friends, and a job I love.

22. Katie Brady

Katie Brady is from Australia and was diagnosed with NF2 in the year 2000 at the age of 21. Katie stresses the importance of informing yourself correctly upon diagnosis and throughout the whole journey with NF2; which can mean not taking anything seen on the internet as fact since NF2 varies so much in each individual and that information is not specific to the person reading it.

In her story Katie entertains us with her various travels and adventures. She proves that you should always believe in yourself and all that you are, and know that there is something inside of you that is greater than any obstacle you have to face with NF2.

Hi, I am Katie. I live in Australia and I am the only one in my family to have NF2. I spontaneously mutated. I have had two surgeries so far to remove tumours. My NF2 journey officially began in 2000, when I was 21 years old. I was diagnosed by a doctor at my local eye hospital with an optic nerve tumour and a meningioma. The scenarios he gave us were not positive. Little did he know... literally. He knew nothing of NF2!!!

My parents refused to accept a negative prognosis, and we waited to meet a doctor from Melbourne. Meanwhile I did the WORST THING EVER – I thoroughly recommend NEVER to do this – and began Googling my symptoms. It came back with a variety of things, among them Neurofibromatosis Type 2. I practiced saying that a lot. Most, if not ALL things you read are negative, worst case scenario type things. Which scared the absolute life out of me. Never Google things, and never read the bad scenarios. EVER!

So I met the Melbourne doctor, who said that he thought I had NF2 – and explained that the tumours were benign, slow-growing and not immediate concerns. He explained things very clearly and took some of our fear away – of course I was still facing a lifelong condition, but the immediate panic was lessened. Through a series of doctors that I saw, one did refer me to my wonderful, fantastic, straight-down-the-line, dry-humoured neurosurgeon in Melbourne – I am so lucky to have this man.

He looked at my scans, and in order to try and save what was left of the slowly diminishing eyesight in the one eye, surgery was scheduled for two weeks later. This was in September of 2000. The day before I left I remember my sister took me out for the most beautiful lunch on the riverbank and I had the most divine pasta carbonara (my most FAVOURITE food). It was so lovely, I always remember her doing this for me.

Four and a half or so hours after surgery began it was over. My tumour had been de-bulked, not removed, as my doctor was trying to do the least amount of damage possible to my nerve to save my eyesight. I did eventually lose my vision in this eye – the nerve was already too damaged.

Thanks to my wonderful parents and then-boyfriend, now husband Jake, I recovered fully, and was back at Uni to start the next year, having missed nothing. I graduated at the end of that year with all my classmates. Yay – Bachelor of Education degree, thank you very much!!! Katie Brady, BEd. Oooh, letters after my name!!! That was awesome – a tumour out and still got my degree on time, thank you very much!!!

In February 2002 I was getting headaches and sharp pains when I moved my head quickly, and had to have a meningioma removed from sort of above my ear on the right side of my head. Back to my wonderful surgeon. Back to Jake sleeping at the end of my bed. Totally removed three hours later. Recovery again. I do feel really rubbish while recovering – dizzy, nauseous, grumpy. But by May I was doing relief teaching, and then in September I got a contract to teach the

Australian school grade 'Prep' – 6 year olds. I have been working as a teacher in the Education Department ever since. So NF2 does NOT have to hold you back from what you want to do.

I have a great, great family, who I cannot thank or speak of highly enough. My parents and my husband are just fantastic. I have a great group of friends, I love to go out to eat – even though my hearing is diminished in noisy situations that is OK. I cope, and get Jake to tell me anything I miss. But I do try to do it myself and lip read in conjunction with my hearing.

I now love to go on holidays – before NF2 I was REALLY scared of flying. OK, it will never be my favourite mode of transport, but hey, life is short, so make it great and have adventures!!!, Jake and I have travelled overseas on holidays many times. We have been through the canals way on the outskirts of Bangkok, Thailand, in traditional longboats (albeit now with outboard motors) to the floating markets. My balance is good, but with my wasting muscle in my leg made getting in and out…. interesting. Same with our elephant ride – hard to get on for me, but I did it and it was really magical - through the Thai jungle!!! We toured the palaces and temples - managed all the steps…whoo hoo!!!

Our second overseas trip was to Malaysia. We stayed first in Kuala Lumpur at the most magnificent hotel that has breathtaking views of the Petronas Twin Towers – just absolutely divine. We toured those, though thankfully you take the elevator not the stairs – I am all for stairs to keep my muscles working as well as possible, but that would have been a bit excessive, even for a person with two 'proper strength' legs. We also rode in those bicycle carts to a fish spa, where fish nibble the dead skin off your feet. Hard getting my leg in and out – but another tick for me!!!

The next trip was to Vietnam and Hong Kong, with a day trip into mainland China. Hong Kong was great – busy, smoggy, but actually pretty physically clean. Most challenging thing in Vietnam from an NF2 person's point of view; we stayed in Hanoi (EXTREMELY busy town – scooter/ motorbike madness – watch out crossing the road). Because they are so noisy and tooting all the time, plus with my limited hearing, you can't tell if they are tooting at you or just in general, so I just assume it is someone else, and go on my merry way. I even crossed several times by myself. Nothing I can't do!!!

Our next trip is by ourselves (Gasp) in July of 2013. We are going to Greece, Italy, France, Germany, Holland, England – where I am a bridesmaid in my school friend's wedding – and Dubai. I am so looking forward to that. I am going on tours of EVERYTHING I can. I am also going to do my best to learn a few sentences in each language of the countries we will visit. Then if I don't hear what they say, I can pretend it is a language thing, ha ha. It will be interesting too, because my hearing has dropped a little more since my last trips. I say that this just means Jake will have to do all the talking and organising, and I can just laze around. Ha!!! My point of all this – I have NF2, but it doesn't have to stop you doing what you want. You can still do anything, just make adjustments. I can curl up and cry and worry and rage, or I can live life. I know which one is more fun, I have tried both.

I still have 2 meningiomas in my head, but have lots of little other ones in there on the periphery that could eventually turn into something, but thankfully they have been stable for a long time. I also have my two ANs still and a tumour in my spine at C1. Again, they are all stable. But I have stuff to deal with.

As for how life is with NF2 – speaking personally, my life is absolutely great. I still teach full time. I have had to change from classroom teaching to Flexible Learning now, as I am deaf in one ear and losing hearing in the other. Flexible Learning is sort of like internet based learning, as even though I can still hear a reasonable bit, I can't hear well enough to be in a busy classroom anymore. I am not losing my hearing from growth from my ANs, they haven't really changed, just from the damage an AN can do just by sitting on the nerve. I'm unlucky in the fact that my ANs are in a really bad spot, because they are actually very tiny. In a different position, they would be having no impact at all. But I love this job, and would never have done it without the issues caused by NF2. Would I rather I didn't have them? – YES!!! But life is still great, just different to how I originally planned.

I live a normal, happy life. Ok, I use captions for TV, and text instead of phone call, but that works for me, and I love my life. I still have so much fun. I have the most wonderful little nephew and niece, who are learning sign bit by bit. Isobel, who is 4 years old, is an absolute champion at it. Basic sign, but she is good. Sam, my 6 year old nephew, is also going well (he tells me his mum needs to practice with him more, ha ha). They are so much fun to play with, pick up from school, and just seeing them puts a smile on my face. I adore them, and they make life even more enjoyable.

A diagnosis of NF2 is NOT all doom and gloom. I walk relatively normally, outwardly look normal and haven't had surgery since 2002. Maybe I will need several big ones soon, maybe I have another twelve years surgery free, maybe I will never need another one. I don't know, no-one does, but I am going to try not to worry overly about it. Whatever happens, I will get through it. I know from experience that sometimes NF2 whacks you over the head with a giant steel pole, repeatedly, and I still have more than my fair share of head lumps (I am not overly fond of the word tumour) that I need to be conscious of watching, but you deal with it, pick yourself up when you need to, and continue living. Not only that, enjoy living. Don't waste days worrying about what might happen. It might not. Then you have wasted all those wonderful days worrying. And NEVER, EVER Google anything about your condition or read the bad stories. You are you. No-one else can tell you your story.

Sometimes I forget I have NF2. Not often, but there are times. Whatever happens, you adjust, and life is great.

23. Keith Straker

Keith Straker is 56 years of age and from Northumberland, UK. Keith underwent a number of surgeries prior to his diagnosis of NF2, whether they were NF2 related or not is unknown. Keith takes us on his journey through these surgeries, eventually leading to the diagnosis of NF2 at 48 years of age.

In his story Keith also talks about the responsibilities of being a parent, the need to make a career change due to NF2 related difficulties, and the importance of seeking support from every available source during times of change.

I discovered I had NF2 at the ripe old age of 48, in 2004. It was by accident that the discovery was made, when I was at the Freeman Hospital in Newcastle upon Tyne getting a check up on a recent operation.

I had been operated on a number of times since I was 17 – a lump on the reverse side of a neck muscle; a lump on the side of my neck which was attached to my carotid artery and in a net of nerves so a particularly precise surgical requirement was needed. In thinking it might be cancerous they looked into my nose & throat, where they discovered a polyp, 'which shows signs of possibly turning cancerous', so that one required surgery to strip out my sinus on that side. "We don't want that coming back so we're going to perform this radical surgery". It came back a year later, requiring another operation.

So it was when visiting the Newcastle Freeman Hospital to have a camera stuck up my nose I thought it would be a good time to mention I hadn't had the results of a recent MRI scan on my head. I was in a professor's clinic along with eight medical students observing the prof's day.

She said she would try to find out, and left the room to return two minutes later saying she had the scan results in her hand.

She sat down and said "I don't know where to begin". Call me a pessimist but I felt this was not leading to a good place. She then went on to read out what seemed like a catalogue of things they'd discovered, including 'growths' and a nice little aneurysm in my brain. Hooray, I had a brain!!

I thought the mood of the room needed lifting so carefully chose the words "So am I going to snuff it?" The varied look on the students' faces made the considered words worth it - they didn't know whether to laugh or cry. Of course, another radical operation on my head followed and the aneurysm was 'clipped' and made safe without loss of life, although I did lose my sense of smell. Having a teenage son and young 'drinker' daughter in my house, as a single father I considered this a blessing. I consider the loss of the smell of curries and fresh-cut grass to be the greatest, but according to the women in my life it should be the whiff of their perfume!

The two auditory tumours meant I had NF2 of course, and thus began the path leading to where I am today. I wonder how many of the previous operations (I've only mentioned the most notable) were NF2 related. For my children's' sake I needed to know what the chances of this being passed on were, but all evidence (lumps) from previous op's had been binned, and they still haven't identified the offending cell(s)/gene which caused this. I'm the first in the family and I have mosaic NF2, meaning it's not in every cell and is difficult to pinpoint (or something).

So where do I begin to tell you about my experiences having NF2? I'll begin by saying my varied and often difficult life experiences AND having children allowed me to not worry about myself. After all, I was 48 and had sewn my wild oats. I was very concerned my children would inherit this, and if this was the case I was told it would be a lot more severe.

I have to say that my experiences of NHS care related to this condition have been varied. Whilst appreciative, but not in need of, the support network I was immediately offered, I found the information and effort of the medical team around me somewhat lacking at times. For example, they strongly advised me to tell my children (at the ages of 15 & 12) what I had, and that they might get it too – along with how this would disrupt/possibly ruin their lives. There was absolutely no way I was going to burden them with such fear and possibly destroy the happiest years of their lives with such news. But that was my decision with my children I hasten to add. My kids are now 23 & 20 & have no sign of it thank God.

I could tell you about my feelings, concerns and inner self, but each of us copes differently with situations. My disappointment is that I've had to work hard to achieve things from my medical team. It was I who suggested hearing aids; I who asked for blue-tooth – and was refused. I found the greatest assistance came from the Audiology Dept after visiting for six years but eventually hitting on a good'un – a person who went that extra mile and allowed me to trial Bluetooth. It didn't seem to work but she gave me the telephone no. of my local council where I stumbled upon a hearing specialist who has been a revelation. She's organised 'Link' in my living room, allowing me to hear the television without the need for sub titles, and amplified telephones with Bluetooth for my business calls now I work from home. All within four or five weeks. Also, with the help of my new specialist nurse, I have just qualified for DLA (Disability Living Allowance) at the middle rate. This gets me £50/week, but more importantly opens up doors to many other things … oh, and cheaper rail travel for me and a 'friend'.

As the condition continues my hearing worsens, along with my balance, but I'm not too bad. I occasionally stumble, and as they warned me, more so when it's dark or I'm tired. I've almost fallen out the bath a couple of times when standing to shower & close my eyes to wash my hair, but the solution for this is either a free service from the council again – to change my conditions – perhaps remove the bath and fit a stand-alone shower unit, or fit grab-rails in the shower. My suggestion of a 20-year-old Swedish Au Pair to be by my side in the shower to catch me met with a frosty response!

So that's where I'm at right now. I had to give up working in an office because I couldn't hear people on the phone with surrounding noise, and now work from home, but love the freedom it brings. The extra hours are enjoyable because I reap the reward of this hard work, and my earnings have gone up. When I become too deaf to use normal phones or use phones at all 'Access to Work' is a scheme that helps provide equipment – or a person - to allow you to carry on working.

I went to Eastbourne in 2011 courtesy of Hearing Link and met others in similar and different places on this journey, including the wonderful Jess, who is compiling this 'book of stories and experiences'. It not only made me realise how lucky I am, but introduced us to both people and equipment: Sign teachers, lip readers, hearing dogs, lights and vibrating pagers to alert you to telephones, fire alarms, door-bells etc. In fact, the most amazing discovery was the text phone. It introduces a third-party to a telephone conversation if you are deaf, and that person types the response of the person you are calling, so you talk, they talk, and you read their response. If you are reading this and have NF2 I urge you to go on a Hearing Link programme when invited. I think it could only be improved by not forcing us to sit together on a long table reserved for the 'deaf gits and their carers'.

To sum up, there is everything you need to ensure you can live comfortably with NF2, and every aspect of support that you may require…. but you may need to ask for it before it's offered.

24. Kerry O'Shea

This story has been written on behalf of Kerry O'Shea by her brother Anthony O'Shea.

Kerry very sadly passed away during the production of this book at the age of 31.

Kerry was diagnosed with NF2 at the age of 16, and despite an abundance of NF2 related challenges she was always an insiration to those around her with her wonderfully unique personality.

Doctors first discovered Kerry's tumours at about eight years old and she was diagnosed with NF2 when she was about 16 years old. In all Kerry had six operations to remove tumours from various parts of the body plus many different operations on her eyes.

Through all this her attitude remained amazing and she was an inspiration to us all. Kerry was the youngest of four children and always viewed as the baby of the family, but this did not stop her being one of the most vocal!! Our mum died in 1996 and in some ways it seemed to hit Kerry the hardest, but Kerry's illness also helped to gel the family together.

Kerry had many interests including line dancing and bingo, plus she enjoyed travelling to various locations around England. As I said I always looked at my sister Kerry and my troubles seemed insignificant; she taught me a lot about acceptance and gratitude. Kerry is a much loved special individual and has inspired me in many ways indeed - I am running the London marathon in 2013 in aid of The Neuro Foundation, who work to improve the lives of those affected by Neurofibromatosis in the UK.

25. Krissy Diaz

Krissy Marie Diaz was diagnosed with NF2 at the tender age of 8, she is now 25 years of age and lives in Long Island, New York, USA. In her story Krissy explains how her life came into darkness at first, but how she has found light again through the magic of art.

Krissy graduated in Art Therapy at Grad School in late 2012 and is now beginning the process of professional certification to become an Art Therapist.

My name is Kristina, preferably known as Krissy. I live in New York and I was diagnosed with NF2 when I was 8 year's old. As in half of the NF2 cases, I was a spontaneous mutation in my family. In the same year that I was diagnosed I had stated that I wanted to be an Artist, with a big smile on a video recording from my father asking me about my future pursuits.

Slowly, my world came into darkness. I had my first brain surgery the same year of diagnosis. The following year, at age 9, I had surgery to remove a tumour from my lower spine as I was suffering from excruciating pain. I was an angry and confused kid. It caused me to become rather shy growing up because I had no one I could trust to understand what I was going through. I also had worries of what would follow every time I went to the doctor for an MRI scan. It scared me, and still does today.

I developed a love for animals. I owned many rabbits, hamsters and dogs growing up. I even had intentions of becoming a Veterinarian at one point. Animals couldn't speak, but I felt comfort in taking care of them and providing them with love and warmth. They provided the same in return for me! I have a special stuffed animal of a rabbit that I still keep on my bed today. I picked her out the year I was diagnosed and she hasn't left my side yet. She also comes with me to all my surgeries. I named her 'Hunny Bunny'.

Due to effects of NF2 I completely lost the ability to hear shortly after graduating High School at age 17. I was scared and very mad, but I held on. Learning American Sign Language privately as a senior in high school helped for the better. After completing two years at my local Community College, where I experienced using an interpreter for the first time, I transferred to Rochester Institute of Technology/National Technical Institute for the Deaf in Upstate, NY. Whilst earning my Bachelor's degree in Art and Psychology I explored Deaf culture, love, and in between all of that a dazzling surgery experience followed my enrolment to Graduate school in Creative Arts Therapy.

Art Therapy is a Mental Health profession using the arts as a method to heal. Psychology became interesting to me when I experienced an acquired short-term brain injury (that 'dazzling' surgery experience I just mentioned) due to NF2 in the winter of 2008. The tumor was located in the 3rd ventricle of the brain, a rare location for an NF tumor. I had short-term memory loss with delusion for two months and a near death experience from a CSF leak in the brain. I knew this profession as an Art Therapist was for me because it was always right in front of me at NYU Hospital where my doctors were, and I never even realized it. I was never sure of my path as an artist until experiencing that surgery.

Art Therapy is so interesting to me with the symbolism of objects. I dug deep in depth of the symbolism of rabbits based on Jungian Psychology by taking an Art Therapy class called Sandplay. Sandplay uses objects placed in a sand tray and sometimes water. Its natural atmosphere creates a way to express using symbolism. I find it interesting how the Rabbit is linked to the moon, therefore a symbol of night-time.

For many years I have been experiencing a lot strain with light as a result of my Acoustic Neuroma (AN) surgeries. My eyes are very photosensitive and I feel more comfortable in dim lit atmospheres. I have very large eyes and was nick named Tweety Bird growing up because I twittered my eyes, as it was one of my favorite cartoons.

My rabbit doll is my omen; she has survived both the good and the rough times with me. Although she's dirty and falling apart, 'hunny bunny' is still intact! Even the real life rabbits I have owned had qualities I would gain when I became deaf. They had the ability to be alert and aware of their surroundings at all times before advancing onto something. They were always cautious and curious. I feel this translates into recognizing that we have the power to create with our thoughts. I began to accept my deafness with a positive force full of curiosity.

During Sandplay using the rabbit, I surrounded her with a flower and a rock in the sand. I find flowers to be very symbolic in my life and although it wasn't my favorite flower (the Snowdrop) the color resembled it in pure white. It means hope. The rock gave me a symbolic feeling of strength. The rock symbolizes human nature, and I found that interesting as I read it because I joined forces with two opposites: Animal instincts and Human nature.

This related to Jung's shadow aspect. The Shadow is considered to be a collection of inferiorities of the personality. I am not always a happy camper, but I always overcome my inferiorities of being one that is "sick" or 'different' because I am aware of it and I don't want 'evil' to take over my life. I feel when you own and accept your shadow (in my case, my illness); you will be healthier and happier.

As I grew up having NF2 from a child and into a teen, in which surgeries and doctor appointments became an agonizing routine, I started reaching out to others going through similar issues. I have travelled to Texas, Michigan, and Florida connecting with the NF2 community and learning that there is so much more to life than simply having NF2, so much laughter and good memories. I thank God for having them in my life.

It is in our times of hurting, especially on the inside, that we need love the most in order to heal and grow because it often becomes negatively expressed outwardly. Precisely this started with me at a young age due to feeling isolated because of NF2. It is important to focus on yourself with truth above all things. Expressing your feelings and expressing your life. However, the rough times we face together can always be overcome and we usually end up building something stronger.

Art Therapy is very healing to me because I can express myself without words and find a positive way to transform my feelings from negative into positive. We can all find ways to do this within ourselves, no matter the challenges we face.

Although I am not a doctor, I still wanted to somehow be a part of the mission to help find a cure for NF. I became the runner I never knew I could be with the Children's Tumor Foundation's NF Endurance Team. Staying active and supporting your own cause is the best advice I can offer because you never know what it will be like down the road. I was a tap dancer from the age of 3 until the age of 18 when I lost my balance. You see, NF has its downsides, but it also opens you to new experiences that can and will change your life.

I continue to stay active by running and doing yoga to help keep my strength and balance intact. If I do not motivate myself I feel that it causes depression and as a reaction my body feels weak. It's easy to fall into the depression trap when you have a chronic illness. It is a daily struggle. There are also times where I simply do too much and became rather cranky with a lot on my mind. I learned that naps are good for people with NF! However, Yoga is my relaxing challenge. It inspired my interest in meditation and Buddhism as a philosophy.

I always hope for better days and for a miracle where NF can be gone, but until then I will create art, inspire, and go forward with all that God has given me. When I graduated post-graduate school with my Master's in Creative Arts Therapy, it was then that I could finally say that NF2 did not stop me from achieving my dreams.

I have also lived with partial facial weakness from the age of 18, and now at 25 many people could say how I blossomed like a flower coping with it.

Now, my next tasks are as follows. Take charge of myself with personal things that are best for me on my road to happiness, things that I have had to push to the side as a busy student such as having facial reanimation. Find the job I was meant to do in helping others as an Art Therapist. Make time to journey by starting a travel fund so I can explore the world. And above all love, and love those in my life who deserve it.

Never give up.

26. Marianne Oliva

Marianne Oliva inherited NF2 from her father and was diagnosed with NF2 at the tender age of 12. The adjustment to hearing loss was a difficult journey for Marianne, but through it all she persevered until she obtained an MBA and, with the help of assistive tools, has successfully managed to hold down her "hearing dependant" job.

With acceptance of her current situation Marianne claims that she has found peace and that if we begin to look at each breath as a blessing, then suddenly everything in an ordinary life becomes a miracle.

The meeting is not scheduled to start for another 30 minutes but that gives me just enough time to set up all of my transcribing equipment. It is meetings and presentations such as this that I am glad I have a daily three hour train commute to write and rehearse my speech in the preceding days.

I begin to carry my laptop into the conference room from my office and then make a few more trips for all of the wires and cables. Lastly, I carry in the microphone. I plug in all of the equipment and log into my account and await the message on the screen. "Can I call you now?" it reads. "Yes, I am ready", I type. The computer says the phone is ringing and I click on the screen to answer it. "Can you hear me?" I speak into the microphone. "Yes, we are good", is typed onto the screen. Now I am ready for the presentation to formally begin.

This is the work life I always wanted; working in a big city with my business degree leading group projects, making presentations, and participating in decisions in meetings. But this was never the way I envisioned the meetings to be. Nor are parts of my life for that matter; I never imagined being deaf.

My story begins being born the second of two children. When I was 5 years old my father had his own NF2 surgery. I did not really understand it at the time, I just knew he had trouble hearing. Nevertheless, I loved my father so much it did not bother me.

As I grew older my sister got tested for the disease. She did not have it so I figured I would not inherit it either. At the age of 12 I became really sick. It was first believed that I had a bad case of the flu because I had been violently ill with nausea and vertigo. By chance, my mother happened to be with my father who was seeing a specialist that day and she told him I was ill. Once he heard the symptoms he told my mother to bring me in for an MRI. Weeks later it was confirmed that I had NF2 and unbeknownst to me had even suffered some mild hearing loss. One month later I was scheduled for surgery in an attempt to preserve the hearing in one of the ears; however, the surgery showed that the tumor was entangled in the auditory nerve so a decompression was made. I was then told that in three to five years I would be deaf. I was left devastated and brokenhearted.

Three years turned into five years which later turned into twenty-two years before I completely lost all of my hearing. In that time frame I completed junior high, high school, college and graduate school, and entered the work force. But I was simultaneously going through the annual MRI's and hearing tests. My hearing went from two functional ears down to one as I completed college. I was afraid to return back to college with less than one functional ear of hearing but I wanted a college degree so much that I pushed myself to go back until I received an MBA.

Once I became deaf I did not think I would return back to work again because I felt it would be too difficult to do my job. The train commute would be bad enough because I could no longer hear messages on the speakers about track changes and delays. My doctor did not think I could return back either. He thought it was all too much for me. Yet I wanted some normality back in my life. So while I was out on medical leave recovering I decided to research assistive tools that could help me perform my job more effectively.

It has now been two and a half years since my surgery and I have been back to my job as a marketing manager for about two years now with the same commute of over 100 miles a day. My job is still the same as before but this time I use assistive tools to accommodate me at work. My telephone calls are made using captel service. My office voicemail messages are sent to me via e-mail in text form. I also use TypeWell service during meetings and trainings to transcribe speech to text in real time. I plan on staying at the same job until I decide to move elsewhere.

My father continues to be my hero, not only because he is my dad but because of the strength he exhumes. From him I learned that a deaf person could drive, work and shop alone, and do many other things, because life can resume for us with deafness. We are now the first father/daughter ABI multi-channel patients in the world.

I have also become comfortable with my hearing loss and telling people I have NF2. There is no shame in being different from other people. The fear I once had is overtaken with peace. Life is beautiful when you can make the best out of your situations. I know I may never hear any better but I am fine with that. I have learned that my hearing does not determine how happy I am. I am happy because I choose to be happy.

This spring I am taking my first solo vacation across the United States since I lost my hearing. I am ready for this challenge. My life may not be perfect or how I planned it to be but life is what you make of it. I have been through many setbacks in life but they have molded me into a determined woman.

This year it will be twenty-five years since I have been living with NF2, which is well over half of my life. My biggest concern was always how different being deaf would make me and how well I would adapt to the situation. But I have found that sometimes we just have to do things a different way to get the end result. It does not make us less of a person. If anything, it makes us stronger, wiser, and more humble. I will continue to not give up on my dreams and what I want out of life. But most of all, I will continue to never give up on me.

27. Mark Dickson

Mark Dickson was diagnosed with NF2 at the age of 11, he is now 33 years of age and lives in Cambridge, UK. In his story Mark talks about having the confidence to embrace physical differences and to carry on enjoying life despite them.

Mark also takes us through his journey with an Auditory Brainstem Implant (ABI) and explains that although it can be daunting at first, it can also be a ray of hope.

It has only been recently over the past few years that Neurofibromatosis type 2 (NF2) has had a big impact on my life. Until about age 30 I had no real interest of what NF2 was or how it could affect me. Although I knew the name of it and that I had the condition I was by far unprepared for what was to come.

I was first diagnosed with NF2 aged 11 with no previous family history, I am now 33. Doctors first thought it was Hemiplegia when I had my visits to Great Ormond Street Hospital as a child.

An MRI scan revealed I had tumours on my lower spine, which had made my right leg grow slightly shorter and weaker than the left, causing me to walk with a noticeable limp. But this never stopped me doing anything the other kids were doing; if I found something tough I would always teach myself a way to do them differently that suited me and pushed myself that little bit further.

I went through my entire school and college years having only this problem with my right leg. I was always determined to do everything other students were doing, playing sports, going on trips etc. I was never picked on or pushed about in my school years, maybe because I didn't sit back and allow myself to be, I got involved. I had the confidence to show people this was me, accept it!

It wasn't until around my mid-twenties that other changes started to occur. Friends and family began to question my hearing around this time, so we'started making regular visits to the doctors to get my ears syringed. With not having any interest of NF2 up until this point I was completely oblivious that it was down to my condition.

Bilateral acoustic neuromas were discovered on both of my hearing nerves after MRI scans in May 2009. The scans had shown that the time had come for my first surgery to remove the vestibular schwannoma on my right side. This surgery left me profoundly deaf in my right ear but I was fitted with an Auditory brainstem implant (ABI) - an electronic device that would provide me with a sense of sound - as a back-up just in case the vestibular schwannoma on my left side decided to grow.

In November 2010 MRI scans unfortunately had shown growth of the vestibular schwannoma on my left side. This meant surgery for it to be removed was inevitable and would leave me profoundly deaf on both sides. So after this surgery it was time to switch on my ABI to see if I could make some use of it.

The news really knocked me down at first; how was I going to cope with this ABI? Is it going to be any good? Will I be able to understand anyone? Well the truth is, whilst I was losing my hearing with the growth of the tumour I was learning to lip read without even realising it. Talking to people wasn't going to be as tough as I first thought...

The sound I received through the ABI to begin with admittedly was useless; the sound I was getting just seemed like a sort of humming. Every noise sounded exactly the same, whether it was a knock on the door or someone talking. If I'm honest I thought it was pointless, and I would be able to cope just as well without it. But as time passed I was amazed at how things changed. I can now tell the difference between different sounds. It's like learning to hear again and allowing your brain to adjust to the different sounds - the brain is an amazing thing! The ABI is very important to me now. When I'm out it helps me to hear essential things like traffic, and I become a lot more aware of my surroundings. At home I am able to hear the door bell and other essential things like the fire alarm; without it I would be oblivious to all this.

Before my second surgery and approaching deafness I made my friends aware that I would need to use the ABI afterwards to be able to hear anything at all. To begin with I think my friends were a little unsure how to approach me, but within just 30 minutes of them first seeing me one turned to me and said "So is your hearing ok then?" They were amazed as to how well I could cope; now they speak to me just as they did before. Occasionally my friends and family will forget that I still need to lip read though and they'll say something with their back turned or even ask me a question about the latest music!

I still find it difficult to talk to certain types of people; for example, I find it hard work to talk to anyone with a large moustache and people with heavy accents can also be a challenge. It was only recently I visited family up North and I struggled when a family member said the word "Car". To me it sounded like the word "Care" but after I asked them to repeat it the sentence made sense. But it is much easier to talk to people now with the ABI switched on; lip reading becomes easier, and there have even been times when someone has asked me a question and I have not been looking at them and I have been able to understand. I am still learning to hear again, and my brain is still adjusting, so hopefully in time there will still be room for more improvement.

It was around the time that my ABI was switched on that I really started to learn about NF2 and what it was all about. In mid-2011 I was informed I had a number of tumours at the top of my spine and that if they grew they could cause multiple problems throughout my body. With this, I was offered a type of chemotherapy treatment called Avastin to try and stabilise them, and so far this has been successful.

I am fully aware that NF2 may continue to throw these kinds of hurdles at me in the future, but I also know through the experiences I've had in life with NF2 so far that any problems I face can be overcome if I deal with them the right way and never let them beat me.

Life with NF2 can be hard at times but it has taught me that, really, I can do anything, I may just have to go about it a slightly different way to how others do. It may look a bit strange, but if I reach that goal at the end...... who cares what people think?

28. Mark Kenny

This story is a wonderful tribute to the late Mark Kenny (1963 – 2005) written by Jean H Pless, formerly Kenny, from Scotland.

Jean captures Mark's story in a way that can go on to inspire future generations with his light-hearted approach to life and sheer determination to never give up fighting.

Also included is one of Mark's many creative poems centred around his journey with NF2.

Mark was born one of ten children (in 1963), but the only one with NF2. When the others were asked to get tested comments such as "never heard of it so I don't have it" were made. Mark was born in Scotland but was brought up mostly in Wales. He left school and became a baker like his dad. He moved to London to work.

While in London Mark's epilepsy got worse; he had Encephalitis as a child, which had given him the side effect of epilepsy. The doctors sent him for a scan and there they discovered an acoustic neuroma. He decided then to move back to Scotland to be with his parents. His health declined a bit and he lost his hearing. After then Mark went to college, and that is where he met me. He was doing an HNC in Computing and I was his Scribe/Note taker. We got married three years later in 1994.

In 1996 we went to Freiburg in Germany for an ABI (Auditory Brainstem Implant). I remember one of the doctors coming out after the surgery saying he was looking good for the camera (they filmed it so it could be used for the future). In Mark's last five years of life his health declined further - I gave up working full time to stay at home and look after him full time. In 2005 we moved to be nearer his mum; she gave me a lot of support, I didn't get it from elsewhere. Two days before we were due to move Mark went into hospital with pneumonia. His health really deteriorated. He came back ten weeks later to his new home, but nearly a week after he was back in hospital. Five days later at 22:14 on 4th June 2005 he died. He died of aspiration pneumonia and complications of NF2.

Mark had a very bright outlook on life - never let anything let him down. If he wanted to do something he went ahead and did it - didn't let disability stop him. He had a wicked sense of humour. When Mark had hearing he loved the band Queen. I remember before he died he said that he wanted the "Birdy song" played at the funeral. He loved his computers and would be amazed at all the technology there is about now. We went to every NF2 get together; he felt the NF2 gang were like another family where everyone understood what it was like to be like him.

Me & You & NF2
by Mark Kenny

It meant nothing to me when the doctor gave his final diagnosis,
"You have a condition called Central Neurofibromatosis".

A faulty gene it seems, on chromosome 22,
But it would be some years before I knew
Simply to call it NF2.

And that it can't be cured nor controlled
And that each case is different in old
Or young, with a family history or a spontaneous one,
But the battle is on – it MUST be won.

The tumours can grow on any nerve
And the problems can be numerous.
But the one thing that is for sure
Is that none of them are humorous.

Space for let:
Short-term leases preferred – might consider long-term.
Any "lump" causing trouble faces eviction.

In SOME cases all hearing is lost,
This causes much pain
For those suddenly realise
They're unlikely to hear again.

But for the lucky few for whom
Circumstances allow another try,
There is some hope with the ABI.
But so far the three ABI's – Andrew, Burt & I –
Have had very different results;
For me, it's either "clangy" or it's "croaky",
But it's still better than I thought it would be
And I would certainly recommend it,
If anyone was to ask me.

Offspring or not, the choice is personal, but
It really does need a lot of thought
Because the chances are even of passing it on
From mother or father to daughter or son.
Unfortunately so, not all had that choice,
They were diagnosed late and already had girls or boys.

I know about me, but what about you?
Cos' some can cope with NF2.
But try not to worry, what good will that do?
After all it will still be with you.
And so before depression sets in,
Put on a smile and lift up that chin.

29. Mark Ramsey

Mark Ramsey is 17 years of age and hails from Northern Ireland. Mark attends a specialist deaf school in England and is studying with the hope to become a doctor.

In his story Mark tells us about his various hobbies and active lifestyle, which he has no intention of changing in his subsequent years.

My name is Mark Ramsey and I was diagnosed with Neurofibromatosis Type 2 (NF2) when I was 5 years old, I am now 17 years old.

I had two tumours growing inside my head. I went to the hospital in Manchester and got told I would need surgery to remove the tumours. When I was 10 years old I had surgery on the left side of my head to remove one of the tumours and because of that I lost my hearing in that area.

It was one year later that I was told I would now need surgery on the right side to remove the other tumour. Since then I have been completely deaf. I was assessed for an ABI (Auditory Brainstem Implant, kind of like a cochlear implant only connected to a different part of the brain). When I got started with the ABI it was really difficult because a lot of the sounds where just beeps and buzzes so it was hard especially in a crowded area as the ABI did not cut out background noise. After four years with the ABI I had it removed as it did not help me all that much.

When I started high school I needed to have a support assistant with me in every class to write down what the teacher was saying and during school I also had a speech therapist come in. Through this I heard about Mary Hare School for the deaf in England.

Although NF2 has had a large impact on my life there have been some good things come from it. At Mary Hare I have met some of my best friends ever and I am now studying for my A-Levels to get into university to become a doctor. I hope to specialise in either Blood or if my lip-reading gets better A&E or something like that.

I enjoy playing my Xbox and on my computer, but even with my deafness I still have a lot of hobbies hearing people like doing. I also play various sports such as tennis, table tennis, football and badminton despite difficulties with my balance.

There is an organisation called Hearing Link who run specialist residential programmes for people with NF2 who are challenged with hearing loss. It is also a place to meet other people with NF2 and to find out more information about the condition and other services available to you. The Hearing Link programme was a nice place as I met other people who had gone through the same as me and I saw that NF2 doesn't really affect what you can do when you are older. If you just set your mind to it and hope for it, then it will most likely happen.

30. Matt Hay

In 2011, Matt Hay completed an Ironman triathlon in Sandusky, Ohio, USA in aid of NF research. An Ironman triathlon includes a 2.4 mile swim, a 112 mile bike ride, and a 26.2 mile run. In the last few years he has also completed an Olympic distance triathlon and a half Ironman triathlon. These are tremendous achievements by any measure, but Matt's accomplishments are all the more remarkable because he lives with NF2.

The Hay family has 5-year-old twins and a 2-year-old, all of whom are healthy. Matt is very thankful for his children's wellbeing, and the fact that he can positively shape their image of him: "I want them to think of their dad as the guy that did the Ironman rather than the guy that can't smile all the way or hear very well," he says.

This piece is a summary written by Matt about his accomplishment in completing the Ironman challenge.

Now that I have the medal and photo proof of my finish, I confess that I was really stinking worried about race day. Even as I type these words I feel a little bit of relief (and a whole pile of pride) in the fact that this is a report on my successful completion of the 9/11/11 Ironman distance triathlon, rather than an explanation of a feared "DNF" (Did Not Finish).

Team Hay arrived in Sandusky on Saturday evening for the usual waiting of the lines to get a race number, get weighed in (first sign that it's a long day ahead tomorrow is that they monitor your weight during the race) and drop off my trike. The bike corral is filled with these crazy fast looking bikes, my 35lb recumbent looked like a hippo trying to hide in a room full of cheetahs (second sign that it's a long day ahead tomorrow).

I got up at 3:30 for breakfast, yeah, that's early. Eating too close to the swim start pretty much ensures that one's breakfast will be seen again at some point during the swim. We headed to the beach behind the hotel at 6:30 for a

7am start. My crew chief, Nora, was there to see me off and offer some great advice like, "Stop talking, they're having a moment of silence". What would I do without her? I felt solid on the swim, it was probably my strongest 'long' swim ever with each of my splits being exactly where I wanted, allowing me to finish right at my 1:30 goal.

The bike started strong (note the word "started"), I started to replace worry with thoughts of "I'm really doing this!" Knowing I still had a lot of pavement to stare at the rest of the day (and night) I was pushing at about 75%; a process my friend Oakes refers to as "arousal control". Awesome. This plan worked fine for me for the first half of the ride - a distance I have ridden dozens of times in training before coming home to make pancakes or go watch a t-ball game. But then mile 63 struck. Damn you mile 63. Around mile 60 a long hill was topped with what is called a "false flat" meaning it looks flat... but no sir... it's still a hill but it's just flat enough to make you question why you can no longer break 15mph despite your best effort. If you've seen the movie Ghost ("Sam Wheat!"), you may recall the "bad spirits" being represented by nasty shadows that creep up on the bad guy. That is exactly how I felt. I could feel the shadows of passing mailboxes and "Sweet Corn" signs creeping up on me (yes, creeping corn sign shadows are also a sign that it's a long day). Those shadows carry with them thoughts like "you still have 50 miles AND a marathon to run" or "now you see why Lance didn't ride a recumbent trike in the Tour all those years". These are DNF thoughts.

The last bit of advice I got before race day, again from Oakes, was to stay in the moment. Up until mile 63 I thought this was a "stop and smell the roses" sort of thing people just say. Shame on me. Staying in the moment got me to mile 64, thoughts of all the folks with NF2 that reached out to me got me to mile 65, recalling all the support from friends and family got me to mile 66 and the most wonderful downhill coast got me to mile 67.

The bike leg wrapped up as I pulled back into the corral 7 hours and 20 minutes later. My crew chief was standing there to greet me with smiles after having spent the day braving the roller coasters of Cedar Point as a single rider. I knew I wasn't feeling well when I stood up off the trike but I don't think I realized how bad I was until I saw the way Nora was looking back at me and the way she spoke. Some of you may know that we've had our share of challenges to face together and through that we have developed a pretty good sense of distinguishing between the question "doing ok?" and "Matt, Are You OK"? The difference is subtle, but it's a valuable characteristic to have in a relationship where one of you has a rare, debilitating neurological disorder. I did what any responsible person would do 9 hours into an Ironman and lied. I told her I was fine. Now let's go run a marathon!

This was the first time since mile 63 that I let myself forget the 'live in the moment' rule and take a second to think "I'm TOTALLY going to be an Ironman today". What's up now, corn sign shadows!

It's a strange thing to be working out as the sun rises and still be working out as the sun sets knowing I have 10 miles to run before the event is over. My biggest worry about the sun is that I fall over in the dark. In case that point wasn't clear, I mean I literally can just fall over and not be able to feel myself falling until I hit something (reason #131 why I probably should have stuck with 5Ks). Fortunately, the run was in downtown Sandusky and there was quite a bit of street lighting.

For the whole run, I ate nothing but GU gels. I had cut out caffeine in the weeks leading up to race day so in addition to the 1300 calories I got from the gels (taken every other mile with water and then Gatorade in between) I felt like I had bonged a pot of coffee. Is it normal for your body to vibrate?

At mile 22 my trusty crew chief was there to meet me. In some ways this felt like my finish line because now I knew there was no way I wasn't crossing the actual finish line. I hadn't had my ABI on for 14 hours now, so as Nora and I spoke I'm pretty sure every aid station volunteer was thinking "why is he yelling at that nice girl?" I'm not sure how much sense I was making at the time but I remember her suggesting that I start running instead of walking (now that's a crew chief) and I remember her calling my dad for me. I'm not sure that I have ever worked harder at anything than I did training for this race and I wanted to let the guy that taught me about hard work know that I was about to finish.

Nora tells me 'Eye of the Tiger' was blasting as we approached the finish line, I'm glad it wasn't a song written in the last decade because I could at least sing this one in my head. After what was about a 6:20 marathon, we were able to cross the finish together at the 15:42 mark. I finally had my finish line picture - let's just all pretend I haven't practiced that pose for the last 36 weeks. I don't know what I expected to feel when I crossed the finish line but it was a rare mix of emotion. I was too tired to feel pride and too proud to feel tired.

The hotel was in site at Cedar Point so we headed back after loading up my bike and transition bags full of run/bike/swim gear (there should be a special name reserved for the scent that develops in a transition bag full of dirty bike clothes over the course of the day). I was able to get around on my own after the race and would describe the feeling as more of total body discomfort rather than pain. I took a shower, then a bath, and then another shower. I was hungry but couldn't eat, and tired but couldn't sleep. Nora, however, was asleep before I could find 'SportsCenter' on the hotel TV. I was awake until about 2 in the morning as the adrenaline and coffee pot worth of caffeine finally let go of its hold on me. I ended what was about a 23 hour day by checking email and Facebook. Overwhelmed doesn't do justice to how I felt seeing every message, post, repost, comment, 'like' and instant message (if you left me a voicemail, then at this point it's probably best we just go our separate ways as friends).

I am writing this just a few days after the race because I don't want to forget the details of the day that so often happens when recounting things. But I do know that I'm an Ironman. I'm an Ironman. Really, I'm an Ironman. Mondays have been off days for workouts so it wasn't until yesterday morning when I didn't have to set an early alarm to hit the Y pool that it really occurred to me that the whole thing is complete. I'm an Ironman. My arms are weakened from nerve damage following surgery, my balance is so poor I ride a tricycle, I have back pain from "innumerable" spinal tumors, I can't safely run in the dark, my ipod battery is always dead, I have to wear special sunglasses and goggles because my eye doesn't blink or tear right... and 'I'm an Ironman'!

31. Melinda Pinkerton

Melinda Pinkerton, age 25, was diagnosed with NF2 at 14 years of age after inheriting the condition from her late father. In her story Mel talks about the various outlets she has found to help channel her emotions with activities such as volunteering and art.

Mel paints an honest picture of a journey with NF2 which has both its losses and its gains. Through faith Mel has learnt that for every disability you have, you are blessed with more than enough abilities to overcome your challenges.

My name is Mel. I was born with NF2, but it was not discovered until I was 14 years old. Growing up, I had been told stories about my biological father and how he braved eight open brain surgeries over the course of two years. Mom said NF2 never stopped him from being the husband, father of my two older sisters, and hard worker that he had always been prior to the spontaneous mutation news. NF2 changed everything, yet my parents kept their faith through the good and bad news of every appointment. I never met my father; two weeks after his funeral, my mom found out she was pregnant with me. This is where my story begins.

My mom re-met an acquaintance at her five year college reunion. They exchanged a few letters but their relationship turned a milestone the night I was born. My mom received a letter from "Mr. Mark" - as my sisters called him. He wanted to know when the baby was born and if I was "a boy or a girl." My mom called him that night. They married a year later. He adopted my older sisters and me; my little sister was born three years later.

As I grew older, I was a typical child. I enjoyed school though I was never good at sports. My focus was music. I sang songs at church and was in the musicals. It was my dream to be a singer, but after my voice started to change in the fourth grade, I turned my attention to piano lessons and playing flute in the school band. I loved playing the flute and excelled at it, even playing the piccolo for marching band. I had to stop my freshman year of high school, due to treatments and losing my hearing in the high frequency portions.

My body continued to slowly change. My parents first noticed my walking, as my right foot curves inward and my balance started to become more unstable. Then my hearing started to decline. After seeing a few specialists, they ordered an MRI to see what was happening. November 18, 2002 is when I first heard the news that I had genetically inherited NF2. I was in shock. I had no idea how it would change my life: not only physically, but also mentally, spiritually, and emotionally. Neither of my two older sisters have the disease, though they had to get MRI's for a period of time to be certain nothing sporadic resulted.

I did not have much time to progress through things that year. A month later, I underwent a surgery to remove a tumor that was pressing my spinal cord flat. That spring, I had six weeks of radiation therapy. I also had another six weeks of radiation in my junior year of high school. Radiation has had long term side effects; it caused damage to my thyroid and pituitary gland which cause multiple problems even now - ten years later. In high school I struggled with anger and wanted just to be normal. My friends had a hard time understanding what was happening to my body and because I did not get hearing aids until January of 2005, I missed out on the social aspect as well.

I attended Colorado Christian University in Denver, majoring in Business Administration with an emphasis in Management. I grew in my faith in God during those years; I finally found peace and confidence about living with NF2. I had supportive roommates and friends who encouraged me during the times of steroid treatments, Tarceva chemo treatments (oral) and

Avastin chemo treatments (IV). Apart from studies and campus life, I felt led to volunteer my time working with an after school street church for kids in Denver who lived in at-risk neighborhoods. The kids changed my whole aspect of what it means to serve and to love. On days I felt so sick, just going there and being with the kids made me forget about my own struggles and find joy in their lives as they lived a totally different world from mine. But they too were physically and emotionally hurting. It made me realize that we all go through struggles in life, whether on the inside or the outside.

I am now 25 years old. I have had more chemo treatments, resulting in two deep vein thrombosis (DVT) within a year of each other. Besides the long term side effects such as numbness in hands/feet, curling fingers due to the muscle loss, pain spasms, hearing loss, bad balance, and loss of fine motor skills in everyday activities, I also currently struggle with chronic constipation as the tumors continue to press on the lower spine resulting in nerve damage. I am not one to like big changes, so this is where I struggle most with living with the disease. I am learning that there are ways to still do daily activities independently, but I have to seek out resources or think outside the box to find new ways. I have also learned that it is okay to ask for help.

My family has been above sacrificial, loving and understanding through it all. We are still learning; no family is perfect. The biggest struggle is effective communication, because it affects the balance between letting me live independently and depending on the family in other ways, such as getting to doctor appointments and putting on my compression stocking every morning.

I started a blog to share my experiences about daily living with NF2 in order to help extended family and close friends continue to understand the obstacles I face and how I learn from them. Because I started the blog, I have been able to connect with other individuals who live with NF2. Talking with my doctors or family about what I physically or even emotionally go through on a normal basis is difficult. Things are hard to explain. Talking to an individual who understands what I am saying without my extra explaining of details, has been very encouraging. I was blessed in college to have met two other girls that both lived with NF2. I learned from them and will always remember them.

Every NF2 patient is affected differently by the tumors, treatments, surgeries and side effects, yet we have a common understanding. In high school I felt so alone - no one understood what I went through so I began to put up a wall. The wall represented me as a strong individual; I wanted to show everyone that I could handle every change in my body, doctor appointment and deep questions that lingered in my mind. It was in college that the wall started to fall down as I started to grow in faith and I became more vocal about my life and conditions.

I continue to remind myself not to build the wall. In being honest with others, whether in conversation or through my blog, I am being honest with myself. Over time I see the growth in my life - the challenges I have overcome and the blessings I have received. It is through these experiences that I am given an extra measure of peace and grace to continue the journey.

I have been trying to make it a habit to see the little blessings in everyday life: Seeing the birds outside my window; writing a card to my grandparents; playing "catch-the-string" with my cat; eating a fresh avocado with sea salt; reading a chapter out of a good book; smelling morning coffee; and painting. After graduating from college, I found that I was angry because I had "lost" my mobility to play and hear music. My life felt boring. I was still working with the kids downtown, yet, I wanted that extra touch of joy and passion in my life that music once brought.

March of 2010, I decided out of the blue to paint a picture for my dad's birthday. A simple bird painting sparked a new passion in me to paint more - painting for my friends and family. It was a new world of opportunities! My best friend got involved and painted with me, while encouraging me to continue to try new styles.

I look back on it now and see how far I have come since then. It has been a rough journey, but a blessed one. Music still holds a special place in my life, even though I know there will be a time when I will no longer hear it at all. Through my paintings I have been able to share my story with others in ways that I could have never imagined. It has been such an incredible experience! I now paint with hope, because hope grows.

I don't know what my future holds in living with NF2, but I do know that I want to continue to grow in faith, learn, serve and love, and paint. These are my aspirations.

To read more: http://mylifewithnf2.com

32. Michelle Jesberg

At the age of 34 after a pre-op MRI scan Michelle Jesberg was diagnosed with NF2 on the day of her first brain surgery. After an initial bout of treatments Michelle began to build her life up again and is now fulfilling her dream of running her own hairdressing business.

Michelle's busy schedule is also filled with volunteer work, a passion for golf, and three children at the heart of everything she does.

I was diagnosed with NF2 at the age of 34 (2004), four months after having my third baby. I was deaf in my right ear at that stage but never really thought to have it checked as my life was busy with two other children.

I was working at the time managing a large building complex in Brisbane City. I took this job on six weeks after having my third child. I was an on-site property manager so I fitted my work in with my family and of course a new baby. The job was flexible and I did really enjoy the challenge of managing a complex of 150 units.

My health had started to deteriorate a little whilst pregnant. By that I mean I was suffering with what I thought at the time was migraines. Of course whilst pregnant I couldn't take any strong medication so I did really suffer.

The turning point for me was one weekend when my youngest was four months old. I had this headache that wouldn't go away, it started on the Friday and by the Sunday morning I was very ill. My symptoms were vomiting, stiff neck, plus this massive headache. They admitted me for a few hours and put me on a drip as I explained to them it was a migraine.

After those few hours I started feeling better so asked if I could go home as I thought that's obviously fixed it up. By that afternoon I was vomiting again with the headache back. I presented to the hospital again that night and the doctor I saw said, "We might just do a CT scan just to check that there's nothing nasty in your brain". What they found was a 4cm meningioma. I had swelling on my brain as well as fluid. They called a neurosurgeon in and he told me the news that I had a benign brain tumour that needed to be removed. It was stressful as I had always thought a diagnosis of a brain tumour was like being handed a death sentence. I mean wow I had a four month old baby, an eight year old daughter, and a ten year old son, I couldn't die.

The next day surgery was scheduled. I had an MRI scan to get me ready for surgery then came the next bit of news….. I not only had one brain tumour, I had many. They were on my hearing nerves (hence the deafness) and a few scattered throughout my brain. He then said you have Neurofibromatosis Type 2. He had to write it down for me as well as sound it out for me. I had never heard of anything like this and thought instantly I'm on my own. The feelings I had whilst in that hospital were dreadful. They said then 1:35,000 had this condition.

Since that time I've had Stereotactic Radiotherapy (2005) on my Right Acoustic Neuroma - which I feel after seven years has been successful - as well as numerous surgeries on my left arm for Ulnar nerve tumours.

I never had any symptoms of NF2 in my young years and I am thankful I was never scanned. I really enjoyed my late 20s and early 30s. I had a fabulous job, two beautiful children, and my new husband and I decided to get married and have a baby together.

Prior to my diagnosis I completed an apprenticeship in hairdressing after I finished school. In early 2013 I decided that I wasn't going to wait around any longer to fulfil my dream and have just bought a hairdressing salon and am building my own business again.

I also help out with a women's violence group. I wanted to do some volunteer work and decided that a Woman's Domestic Violence group is what I had a passion to help with. I don't do a lot as time and children are an issue but I do help out when needed.

After my brain surgery and my stint of radiotherapy my family and I decided to move nearer to my husbands' business and we now live on a golf course. My husband always had an interest in golf and took it up nearly straight away. About a year later I decided to take some lessons and start playing. My balance has never been a real issue, but I thought if it is in the future then golf will give me something to try and work hard on to overcome. This has been a fantastic rewarding sport for me. I've won a few tournaments and go out to play weekly. I prove to myself each week that NF2 isn't going to stop me doing what I love and enjoy. I have lots of problems with my left arm, so far I've had six surgeries and the tumours keep growing back. It does make my golf a little harder to play as my left arm won't straighten anymore but I have managed to work with this and not give up.

My three children have been a reason to fight and live for. I've taught all three children not to sweat the small stuff and live life to the fullest. I hope they look at me with pride knowing that although some days it is hard to get moving, with pain sometimes causing me to be frustrated, I just get on and do it anyway.

33. Natalie

Natalie is from Manchester, UK, and was diagnosed with NF2 at 13 years of age. In her story Natalie shows how sometimes fear of the unknown can get in the way of making the right decisions for ourselves.

Natalie was burdened with a huge amount of NF2 related challenges at a young age but she has found her way back to both health and happiness.

My name is Natalie. I've just finished a degree in English Language & Linguistics. It's not been an easy road to get here though. This is my story:

I was diagnosed with NF2 when I was 13 years of age. I was a fit and healthy teenager, so when I began having problems walking, it was obvious that there was something wrong. A scan showed a large spinal tumour. A few days later, I had emergency surgery to remove it and that's how I was diagnosed with NF2.

A year later, I had my first acoustic neuroma removed. I lost the hearing in the left ear but it didn't affect me at all; I was back at school within a few weeks.

For the next seven years I had no problems. I had a boyfriend, a part-time job, did my A-levels and started university. I had a fantastic life and I put my NF2 to the back of my mind.

Doctors had been telling me for a couple of years that the left acoustic neuroma had grown back and both acoustic neuromas were now very big and needed to be removed. But I wouldn't listen. I refused to have them removed because I couldn't bear the thought of being completely deaf. This turned out to be the worst decision I've ever made.

A week after my twenty-first birthday, I had surgery to remove a tumour from my brain stem; I didn't walk again for eighteen months. It was like my whole body had shut down - I couldn't walk, I couldn't eat or drink, I couldn't do anything for myself. My hearing was declining rapidly and I also had facial paralysis. Looking back, I probably shouldn't have had the brain stem surgery whilst I had two massive acoustics neuromas there, it was just too much pressure.

In the following few years I had both of the acoustic neuromas removed. I had a facial nerve graft on the left side and it was starting to work. So I was devastated after surgery for the right acoustic neuroma to discover that I had facial paralysis on the right side too. But the surgeon reassured me it was temporary.

It was the hardest time of my life and there were times when I couldn't imagine ever being happy again. But I never gave up; I wasn't going to let NF2 ruin my life. I pushed myself spending hours in the gym every day. And with a lot of hard work my walking gradually returned to normal. I was extremely lucky that over time, my face did too.

I was completely deaf but after everything I'd been through I knew I could deal with it, and I was certain that it wouldn't stop me from doing what I wanted to do.

Fast forward and I've just graduated from University with an English degree and in September I'll be starting a Master's degree. I like to go horse riding and rock-climbing, and I still go to the gym. I've got a gorgeous boyfriend, lots of friends, and once again I've got a fantastic life.

There is no doubt that NF2 can be a devastating condition, but I feel incredibly lucky to be living in a day and age when we've got fantastic technology like subtitles, text messages and emails.

I feel lucky that we've got amazing surgeons and that since the age of 13 I have been fortunate to be under the care of a Professor whose dedication to NF2 patients is inspirational.

Having NF2 and being deaf isn't going to stop me doing anything I want to do. If anything, it's made me more determined. The sky is the limit.

34. Nathalie Trytell

This piece is a beautiful tribute to the late Nathalie Trytell, written by her family, which will live on in memory of a talented artist and inspirational person. Also included is one of Nathalie's wonderful creative poems.

Nathalie Trytell (1979-2011) a poet, painter, artist, and printmaker lost her life to Neurofibromatosis (NF) type 2. Her spirit was stronger than any obstacles she faced and Nathalie went on to receive her degree in Art from the Massachusetts College of Art and Design. Nathalie lived life to the fullest; her wit and captivating presence shone a bright light on all those around her. She was a vibrant and creative soul who inspired the many people lucky enough to come into her universe. The poem below encapsulates some of Nathalie's fondest memories; taking road trips and being free from the difficulties she faced daily. Her incredible talents as an artist are a treasure and a legacy that remain a beautiful memory.

Untitled poem
by Nathalie Trytell, 2009

In western Massachusetts
I would find my lake.
Water lilies sprouting like millions of old friends in greeting.
Purple Wildflowers swimming across the water and
Blue fish nibbling toes

In Vermont the vast sky would appear over green hills carved by God's hands

Valleys howling like the coyote calls into the wind.
I would find clouds in the shape of gods and goddesses making love,
A wise woman and my sense of smell.

I would find the teasing sun creeping into the morning's window like a curious child

Maine of course would bring me the ocean with its salt air.
Pink granite rock on coasts
Tide pools with red starfish
The sea moving boats gently into the harbor.
Here I'd find my chowder and lobster huts.
My roaring fire pits
And roasted marshmallows
Not to mention ferocious mosquitos.

New Hampshire would neatly fold every place before it and wrap it into silk cloth,
It would include its star lit skies,
Its bay, it's canvas sails,
Its barns and rolled hay
Mount Washington watching over
Nickering horses and fishing villages
It would tie a red bow around the silk like
A package to be sent into the drawers of memories.

35. Peter Crawshaw

Peter Crawshaw now 62 has been deaf since the age of 25. In his working life Peter was a Consultant Radiologist and for 25 years until the present has also been a voluntary doctor for various motorsport events.

In his story Peter stresses the importance of developing optimism and confidence when facing life with NF2, even though it can be difficult.

I trained as a doctor and qualified in 1974. My hearing was deteriorating. Virus damage they said.

Less than two years later, on my stag night, I fell down some stairs and woke up to a severe hangover and almost total deafness. A CT scan, on one of the two machines then in Britain, showed large acoustic neuromas. A double operation, total deafness, and time in intensive care followed. I had previously obtained a training post in Radiology. My new professor insisted I take the post 6 weeks after the operation. I struggled with the training, but with massive support from my wife and teaching staff, as well as colleagues, I eventually became a consultant.

I have just retired after 27 years as a consultant radiologist and latterly a university lecturer. My two children both have NF2 and have had to face multiple operations and deafness.

My work was at a hospital in the Lake District and I was able to enjoy hill walking, and many other outdoor activities. For 25 years I have been a voluntary doctor for motorsport, covering car rallies and speedboat racing usually in remote and beautiful parts of the country. I have also travelled as much of the world as time and money allowed. In my retirement I continue these activities.

Facing NF2 and all its problems is a daunting experience for the patient, relatives and friends. Optimism and confidence are vital but very hard to develop. When I first became deaf I would cross the road to avoid people rather than try to communicate. It took me years to come to terms with difficult communication. Digital communication text, e mail, ipod etc have helped tremendously. When I was on call I used a vibrating bleep and a text phone. For lectures I used power point and my students learned to write questions and pass them to me.

Always declare your deafness. I feel I need a sign round my neck saying I AM DEAF SPEAK SLOWLY AND FACE ME!!

With regard to my disability my patients were always understanding and frequently wanting to discuss their hearing problems. My x-ray and hospital staff were also very supportive, but I faced criticism and impatience from some medical colleagues. Developing a thick skin helps and you need a couple of friends who will share a pint of two after a particularly bad day. Try not to bring too many problems home as your partner is already having to cope with your disability at a personal level.

Find activities which you can enjoy and which will relieve the stress. Fishing, walking, travel, cooking, meals out, reading, computer work, gardening running, climbing etc are all possible without too much communication.

Films (videos with subtitles), theatre (difficult), charity work, church, and pub socialising mean that you can join partners and friends as well as making new contacts. Fast driving (safely) and off road driving are great for relieving stress but a rather expensive option.

Learn your limitations at work and socially. By and large try to live within them. Just now and then push a bit and see how far you can go. You can do most things but you need lateral thinking. NOT 'I cannot do this', but, HOW 'can I do this'.

A couple of years ago I was one of the Medical Officers for our International car rally in the Welsh mountains. Six modified landrovers from the UK armed forces competing against each other brought up the rear of the rally. On my stage one went missing and I drove through at speed to find it on its side in a deep ditch. The two crew members were unhurt, sitting on the top of the 15 feet high bank. With difficulty, I climbed up to check them over. The driver a big fit guy was fine. The co-driver was an officer previously injured in Afghanistan. He had one arm and no legs, just short false ones. My balance is poor and I needed help to get down the bank, as did the driver. The limbless co-driver however refused all help, slid down on his bottom, and crawled up the other side. We righted the vehicle and they drove off. When I start to feel sorry for myself I remember that young man and his courage.

36. Poetgirl

In her story Poetgirl, from the USA, talks about adapting to life with NF2 and how although she lives with multiple challenges due to NF2 she still enjoys living life to the full.

Also included is one of Poetgirl's many wonderful poems from her book 'NF2 Living – Win The Challenge'.

What I have learned from having the NF2 disorder are patience, appreciating the simple things in life and thanking and praising God for everything. After one suffers nerve damage, which is common to us NF2ers, either from tumour growth and/or the surgery itself, we lose functions that require much patience in learning new ways of doing things as we adapt to life.

We learn to appreciate the simple things. For me it is making the bed each day from a wheelchair, as well as cooking meals, baking, doing the dishes, ironing, and the laundry - all from a wheelchair. I am blessed I can still do these things. Granted it takes me longer, but I get the job done. In all these things I give thanks and praise to God. I feel His many blessings bestowed upon me each day.

I have always been a person who looked at life as the glass half full, not half empty. I continue to do so from a wheelchair, on a G-tube due to throat and oesophagus paralysis, no voice due to paralyzed vocal cords, on 24/7 oxygen, poor vision, and deaf. None of these things have stopped me from living life to the fullest of my capacity and enjoying life

NF2 has not stopped me from living, it has given me strength to live and never give up.

NEVER GIVE UP
by Poetgirl

As we face tomorrow it may seem
slower than slow
But one day will arrive to surprise us
where we feel once again we can go;

Yes, we lose part of ourselves in some surgeries,
a life we once loved and lived;
But we find new talents and ways to adjust
so again we feel we have something to give.

Each bend in the road has its hurdles
Some are easy and some are hard to push through;
But strive on through the stormy waters ahead
And you become stronger in all that you do.

As we "race" on to live life to the fullest
To show our overflowing cup;
We stick together as in our Crew motto
And that is - Never Give Up!

Isaiah 41:6 Every one helps his neighbor,
and says to his brother, "Take courage!"

(NF2 Living – Win The Challenge,
pages 107 and 109, by Poetgirl,
used by permission)

37. Robert Sebastian

Robert Sebastian was diagnosed with NF2 at the age of 12, despite there being signs of the condition since 8 years of age. Robert takes us on his journey with NF2 and talks about how his passion for music has helped him through difficult times.

Whilst a love of music may seem ironic when one is deafened, Robert does not let this stand in the way of achieving his ambitions. Robert recently released his first album which can be found at www.RobertSebastianMusic.com and through this he shows us that no matter how difficult our circumstances, we should never give up fighting for our dreams and what is rightly ours.

I was born on the North Shore of Massachusetts, the third child (and only son) of my Irish father and Sicilian Mother. I had a very normal childhood; fishing, riding my bike, baseball, and recall nothing significant in my life until I was eight years old. While waiting with my mother for a doctors' appointment, my mother had me do the eye chart to amuse me and keep me occupied, and that's the first time I told her I could not see out of my left eye. I had known I couldn't see out of my left eye, but up until this point did not realize it was so unusual.

At my own appointment shortly thereafter it was discovered that there was a tumor on my left optic nerve. The doctors missed my other brain tumors, and what should have been seen as part of the pattern of Neurofibromatosis Type II (NF2) was unfortunately overlooked.

Immediately after the initial appointments I had surgery to remove the tumor on my left optic nerve. My prognosis was that the tumor they had removed was a fluke and my health (and life) would not otherwise be affected.

Later that same year, shortly before my ninth birthday, my family moved to Nashville, Tennessee. My father is a songwriter, and since Nashville is a music hub, there were better opportunities for him to pursue in the South. When we had settled into our first house, I begged my father to set up his drum kit. I quickly picked up the drums, and I eagerly wanted to move on to his electric guitar. Although I have since learned and enjoy playing various instruments, the guitar has been the instrument I play and love most.

When I was twelve I started having trouble in school because I noticed my vision was getting worse. After having more tests done, I was sent to a neuro ophthalmologist, who, after reading my MRIs, learned that there were multiple tumors in my brain, and immediately recognized it as NF2. After another year of testing, they were still unable to explain my declining vision. When I was 13, my doctors decided to do exploratory brain surgery, hoping to discover and resolve my vision problems. I was told my eyesight may improve, but, there were no guarantees and my vision could just as easily worsen. Unfortunately my vision did worsen, and although I cannot notice any difference, my doctors say, as I have gotten older it has continued to decline still more.

In the next year and a half, I underwent two additional surgeries. Both to remove Vestibular Schwannomas that were growing on my hearing nerves. The doctors removed my balance nerves in hope of preventing future growth. They were able to preserve my hearing in both ears, without any damage to surrounding nerves, and both surgeries were viewed as a complete success. My doctors were hopeful that they had removed the possibility of future hearing problems. And for the time being, they had.

When I was 18 a doctor brought up concern over a tumor I had growing on the C2 of my spine. Since I was then considered a legal adult, it was the first time I was really able to participate in the decision making of the procedures that I went through. I was told about a radiation treatment called cyberknife, which at the time, was fairly new. I was interested in alternatives to surgery. I opted for the cyberknife, and it still stands that it stunted the growth the C2 tumor.

In January of 2008, when I was twenty-two, I picked up the phone to call a friend, and put the phone to my right ear, heard nothing, then to my left. I realized I could not hear out of my right ear. My first thought was not "I've gone deaf", because I had MRIs every year, and they had shown no new growths.

The three weeks following my noticing the hearing loss I had significant vertigo. The general practitioner I went to about this ran tests, but found nothing unusual. After factoring in my dizziness and hearing loss, she suggested that I was experiencing the effects of tumor growth, and ordered an MRI. The scan showed regrowth on both of my hearing nerves. I was shocked, because at that point, I was still seeing my neuro ophthalmologist that diagnosed me with NF2 yearly, and he had not even mentioned regrowth at my last appointment.

My mother thought something had to be amiss, and decided to get a copy of my entire history of MRIs. After reading over the radiologist's notes, she noticed, that beginning in 2003, five years earlier, the notes had pointed out regrowth on both of my hearing nerves. The doctor who had diagnosed me had failed to flag these growths, which ultimately led to me losing complete hearing in my right ear.

I learned the hard way the importance of second opinions, and I urge anyone in a similar circumstance to get one. If it's the same, it will only reassure you, if it's different, it will help you consider your options.

Nine months after going deaf in my right ear, I had another brain surgery to remove Vestibular Schwannoma on my hearing nerve, and since I could no longer hear out of that ear, they severed the hearing nerve to remove the Vestibular Schwannoma completely.

In the summer of 2011 I was at a concert and without realizing, got too close to a speaker and suffered significant noise damage to my left ear. This made me re-evaluate everything. This hearing loss was not caused by NF2, but rather, just standing in the wrong spot at a concert, the one time I didn't have my earplugs with me.

It has been very easy for me to give way to thoughts of bitterness at different times because of NF2, but, at least NF2 is predicable, I can expect certain things from the disease. I can read and learn from others from our support group. But, the noise damage I suffered was from just life, which made it almost unbearably manageable.

Music has been a way for me to manage NF2, even when it changes, and sometimes rapidly. I have a creative outlet I can use, to vent both positive and negative emotion. I never realized how much I took my musical talent for granted until the hearing loss I suffered at twenty-six.

Despite challenges, obstacles, social awkwardness, feeling different, loosing confidence, friends, and senses. Despite losing, I haven't lost. Despite loss, I have not lost. I choose to look at this like a Boxer... you can get knocked down, but you're not knocked out... it's just one round. Walt Disney said, "Keep moving forward"

Sometimes you don't like what you're handed in life. You have to make a decision to give up, or get what you want. If there is nothing, you have to build something. Despite it all, I finally finished and released an album, and I plan to do many more. I will keep doing music even with the threat of Vestibular Schwannoma on my left (and only) good ear.

I've always struggled to see myself as more than a man with a disability, but I am slowly seeing myself the way my friends and family do, as Robert, a man, and musician. And now that I am beginning to see myself that way, doors are starting to open, and I am building for myself what I have dreamed.

38. Sally Kingsley

Sally Kingsley is 38 years of age and from Yorkshire, UK. When Sally was diagnosed with NF2 at the age of 27 she was given a very ugly prognosis. As an avid horse rider competing at a high level Sally's world suddenly threatened collapse; but her story doesn't end that way.

Sally's story shows us how her passion for show-jumping and living life to the full is higher, wider, and stronger than any fence she's had to face with NF2.

Here is an overview of my story so far and the message that goes with it, which is that you should always have faith in the future, and confidence in your ability to make the very best of change – even if it looks like adversity at the time.

In 2001 I was diagnosed with two benign brain tumours. I was 27 years old at the time, just two years out of vet school and enjoying a golden life. Earlier that year I'd cycled across Cuba for Guide Dogs for the Blind. I'd just been headhunted for a very high-flying job down south. I had a new boyfriend. I was being filmed regularly for TV (how the cameraman loved my bubblegum pink wedge shoes) and the crew was there when I rode clear over a cross country course at Blenheim 3 Day Event - the biggest international horse trials I'd competed in so far. But then, overnight, my wonderful world threatened to collapse.

I was only diagnosed, by accident, when I went along to a new GP for holiday jabs and he wondered if my occasional dizziness was due to something more serious than a little work stress and too much Red Bull! With my job move I'd had to register at a different practice, meaning a new patient check. The GP had an interest in eyes, and when I mentioned an occasional wobbly feeling when I sat up from being in a horizontal position, plus a tingling in my top lip, he was quick to examine my eyes with a retinal slit lamp. He sent me for immediate MRI – a very on the ball GP.

Doctors told me categorically that I would be totally deaf within two years. Not just hard of hearing, but unable to hear a drum beat, never mind birdsong or a boiling kettle. My family was taken aside and told that I would be lucky to work again after two major bouts of surgery. I would very probably never recover enough balance to walk properly again, never mind ride my horses. My facial nerves would very likely be totally paralysed. It was not a pretty prognosis for someone as active and ambitious as I am.

What happened to me "Shouldn't Happen to a Vet", to borrow a phrase from the late, great James Herriott. But there was no dodging the medical facts - I did have these brain tumours and even though they were benign, they were large and doing a lot of damage to my facial and auditory nerves. Life-threatening treatment beckoned. But I wasn't going to have it steal my lovely lifestyle without a fight.

Ignoring the doom-mongers I made what turned out to be an inspired professional decision: I blew my mortgage protection pay-out on retraining as an equine dentist, spending five months in Idaho and California. Whilst I plumbed the oral mysteries of ramps, hooks and wolf teeth in America my parents scoured the world – literally – for a place to have the surgery with the best statistical results.

I went to Hannover, Germany, and there I spent a month in July 2002, followed by a further month in November 2003. My treatment was a white knuckle ride, involving weeks of very slow and painful recuperation as I had to learn to walk again, and was too ill to eat for two weeks each time. Happily, or unhappily, my appetite returned with a vengeance. Just enough hearing was saved in one ear for me to get by and I did not, as was feared all over Christmas and New Year 2004, go blind. My cheesy smile may not fully return, but I can now give the ghost of a grin and I continue to laugh a lot.

I went back to work in February 2004, to find myself in exactly the right newly fashionable line of work at the right time. Still wobbly on my feet, I took up Pilates; I frightened drivers all over the Dales by running round the road in a very uneven style, and ate my meals sitting on a balance ball. Would I ever ride again? You bet. Last week I jumped a 5ft 6in hedge out hunting. Realistically I will probably never fulfil my dream of riding round Badminton, so my new ambition is to compete at a national championship in amateur show-jumping.

Over the past eight years I've worked tirelessly to improve what I can improve - mostly balance and lip-reading. The latter is still poor, but with pen and paper and iPhone to assist I get on ok. In this time have broken in (trained) four horses, and competed all of them successfully at affiliated level - one to a high level eventing and another has just qualified for his national championship at Aintree. My New Year's resolution/ambition was to stand on one leg - and I'm getting there. Plus I'm now running for an hour each day with the aim of taking part in the Great North Run in 2013. I am lucky to be optimistic by nature – I've always been one of those for whom the glass is not just half but three-quarters full. I was always determined to carry on as if life hadn't crumbled, but it's a lot harder than I envisaged!

When preparing for surgery I focussed on the frivolous details that diverted the mind – like Mac Mascara, Agent Provocateur perfume and the perfect pre-op spray tan. When I was at my worst in hospital, my brother coaxed me into making a wish list. It featured a lot of pink champagne, oysters and weekends in Barcelona. Over the past eight years I've really relished in ticking these items off.

I have to be truthful and say that life is not as peachy as it was, but it's so much better than it might have been. I love my work, my riding and those close to me. I can still be naughty which makes it all the more appropriate that my first dentistry ad to appear in the Yorkshire Post featured the misprint OWN SEDITION, instead of OWN SEDATION. Life is for living and loving and there's no place for a half-hearted approach. I figure that if you keep reaching for the stars and get half way there, you've done a grand job.

39. Sally Richards

In her story Sally Richards, from Chicago, USA, explains that whilst her NF2 related challenges seemed overwhelming at first she has gained strength, courage and confidence through every experience in which she stopped to look fear in the face.

Sally now works for a number of organisations in order to support others with NF as well as herself.

My name is Sally Richards and I've lived with the uncertainties of NF2 for 28 years. Early after diagnosis, my challenges seemed insurmountable, but they proved to be stepping stones to a stronger future. I went from a shy, quiet individual to an articulate, outspoken professional.

I've decided to look at the challenges of NF2 as I would if NF2 were a business. I research and plan and strategize to ensure I make informed, well thought out decisions, rather than letting my heart or my emotions lead me. How do I do this? I work with wonderful organizations propelling action and accumulating resources towards the betterment of NF. I team up with local, national and international organization along with the multi-disciplinary team of NF2 experts at Northwestern Memorial Hospital Chicago, Illinois USA.

The benefits of working with these organizations is two-fold: 1) I'm able to partner with individuals who work tirelessly to achieve a better life for those with NF and, 2) it's life sustaining, guiding me and strengthening my journey through life.

My life focus is: "Prosperity is a lifestyle that includes spiritual fullness, physical well-being, mental soundness, social friendships and financial well-being. It's possessing and stewarding wisely all that God gives to you." I live the motto, "Patience is a virtue, but persistence to the point of success is a blessing."

(Taken from the NF Network website www.nfnetwork.org)

40. Shaunna Kelly

Shaunna Kelly is from Queensland, Australia, and is 46 years of age. In her story Shaunna entertains us with her travel experiences, fun adventures, and the conquering of her limits.

Through these examples Shaunna proves that NF2 does not have to stop you from doing the things you want to do and that life is what we live.

Growing up in Central Western Queensland I was so fortunate to have a childhood full of adventures. I was blessed with a loving Mother and Father as well as three older sisters and one younger brother. We learnt to swim in the muddy waters of our dam and we rode horses, helped with the cattle work and mustering, and had lots of animals

I am certain some of my strengths come from growing up within a close family where we learnt love, respect and gratitude for all that we had. Mum and Dad generously provided us with a wonderful education and love and support in all that we did.

We lived seventy miles out of town and went to the one teacher primary school our parents helped build. In grade one a nurse from the Education Department visited our little school to test everyone's hearing and eyesight. The nurse sent a letter home with me to tell my parents that I had a lazy left eye and that they should get my eyes tested. That was the start of many visits to many doctors.

The lazy eye condition was corrected over the period of two years, but then began a problem with my right eye. Ultimately, Mum and Dad were told the diagnosis of third nerve palsy in my right eye – cause unknown. I had four lots of cosmetic surgery on my eye to try and raise the lid of my eye, as well as fix my eye pupil in a more central position. From around the age of eight years old I learnt to live with looking a little different – my eye would not open as normal.

Many years later in 1999, I was out doing my normal exercise for the day and was running down the track at Mt Whitfield in the middle of Cairns in Far North Queensland. For some time, I frequently heard a noise in my left ear, and it was there again and it was always louder when I ran.

After experiencing really bad and constant headaches for two months, I had a CT scan that showed all clear. My doctor suggested acupuncture to try to relieve the headaches. I went to acupuncture and as well as getting some relief I became a fan for life of that ancient therapy.

Many times I said to my doctor that there was something wrong with my ear and he would look inside it and could not see anything wrong. I went to an ear specialist in Cairns who sent me for a MRI.

The noise in my ear was tinnitus; the diagnosis was Neurofibromatosis (NF) Type 2.

Two months later I had major surgery to remove the first acoustic neuroma (right side) – eight weeks recovery and back to work. I could tell a few yarns about that experience, but it may have to wait until next time.

I went under the anaesthetic reminding my surgeons that I was to be bridesmaid for my sister's wedding in three weeks and for them to go easy on the haircutting!

Fifteen months down the track I had surgery to remove the second acoustic neuroma (left side) – six weeks recovery and back to work – but without any hearing in my left ear since that day.

Throughout the last thirteen years I have had the most amazing support from my wonderful family and some extraordinary friends, and while I have experienced some discomfort at times, I feel like life has been fairly characteristic of the norm. Whilst working for Ansett Airlines I made the most of many incredible travel opportunities and adventures in Australia and overseas.

Balance issues generally are in hand, unless I am tired, in the dark or on an uneven path. Thankfully I mostly forget about those tiny inconveniences. On one occasion where possibly my balance did have an effect on my daily activities, I did not come to any conclusion at the time that it was a problem, until months later in fact.

After my surgery in 1999 I knew I would become a forlorn soul if I was not well enough to travel on a planned snow skiing trip to Canada, three months after my surgery. So while recovering it remained my incentive, to be well enough for that journey to the snow. I decided that I was going to take on snow-boarding for the first time. I can still remember that my butt was black and blue for several weeks after from the many falls while trying to navigate a path down those beautiful slopes at Whistler. Every time I fell over the pain would shoot through to my still fragile head, but nothing would have stopped me from embarking on that truly exceptional holiday.

With stopovers in Vancouver and Hong Kong, enjoying outings to restaurants and bars, hosting dinner parties in our apartment and lots of partying with my friends, it was a special time. Six months later I was talking to my friend about the trip and I said that maybe all the busters on the snow were because of my very dodgy balance. My friend said "I thought of that every day, but I was never going to mention it to you!"

In 2008 my regular MRI proved that amongst a number of other tumours in my head, I had another one on the right acoustic nerve. Having lost hearing in my left ear after previous surgery, that approach was not a consideration. Talk was of radiotherapy – thirty-five days over five weeks or a one off treatment. There were risks involved and it was decided we would not go ahead with that action for now.

In October 2009 I had my routine annual MRI and checkup. As I walked with my Dad to see my neurosurgeon, I jogged my memory of the promise I had made to myself that if there was again no talk of any treatments, I would go on the trip overseas that I had been dreaming of for a long time. I walked out of the appointment knowing that I would be winging my way to Europe sometime in 2010.

My three months away in the UK, Ireland, France and Italy was certainly an outing like no other I have experienced to date. Previously I had been worried about travelling alone, but after the last few years, that fear had dissolved and paled against what had been happening in my life and it was seriously the best decision ever to make into reality.

On my return from my magical trip overseas I was faced with the decision making of whether to go ahead with the one off radiotherapy treatment to try and preserve hearing in my right ear. I really felt like there was no opportunity for a win either way. If I did not go ahead with treatment, I could lose my hearing, if I had treatment, there was the risk of hearing loss as well. I chose to have the treatment. From tumours or treatment, I am left with little hearing in my right ear. Even though I thought I was way too young to have a hearing aid, that little accessory was a life changing purchase.

Headaches, fuzzy heads and debilitating exhaustion have made life interesting in recent times. My specialist doctors agree that I am 'normal' for my condition and that continuously concentrating on trying to hear would to a certain extent add to my fatigue. Financially, it was not a favourite option, but I have bitten the bullet and taken the opportunity of part time work, and I really hope that heading down this path will lend a hand in effectively managing these symptoms.

I just have to tell you about a trip a couple of years ago when I enjoyed another exceptional and entertaining trip to the snow – this time to Japan. There were twenty of us and it was without a doubt one of the funniest trips ever. My tummy muscles hurt – not from trying to snowboard, but from laughing. I do not know if it would be called snowboarding what I did on those Tsugaike Kogen slopes, and I do not know if I can convey in words my feelings on my first day and every day after on the snow. I am not very good at snowboarding – put it that way. But the fact that I was able to get down those runs (with a few busters), and get back on the lift to the top again was a dream. And as I sat strapping my boot into the snowboard, I was overwhelmed with exquisite joy and euphoria that I was sitting on that mountain with spectacular conditions and getting ready again to glide (I am trying to make it sound like I am good now!) through the snow and make it to the bottom. I thought every day and every breath was a gift, I thought if I can do this, I can do anything.

So I try and tell myself the same, often. Sometimes it all seems overwhelming and I do not know what the future holds for me. I read enough and see enough to know that there are so many more people worse off than myself. I have no doubt that life is what we live, and nobody gets to the end without some suffering. I know in my heart and my head, that I have to just get on and make the most of what I have and not worry about what may be missing or what may be lost.

41. Steve Silverman

Steve Silverman, MA, is 57 years of age and from Los Angeles, CA, USA. Steve's journey with NF2 began when he was 27 years of age, when the condition was formerly known as von Recklinghausen disease.

In his story Steve shows true fortitude by refusing to bow down to NF2. Despite an abundance of challenges Steve continued teaching until retirement and has worked with a number of organisations in order to support and benefit others with NF2.

"Am I going to die?"
"Probably not."

This terrifying exchange was between the radiologist who first identified my cranial tumors and me. At age 27, married, with two toddlers and a five year old teaching career, I knew I had some loss in my right ear. At age 19 doctors told me that I had a mild loss, from a virus I'd had that would probably never get better and probably never get worse. Wrong!

An earwax plug on the left made it clear that the right was contributing nothing, and a follow-up with an ENT showed no function there beyond the shadow of a normal left ear responding to bone-conducted loud sounds on the right. The ENT ordered a precautionary CT scan, technology so new in 1982 that I had to schedule my appointment for a day when the van that carried the machine from hospital to hospital was at my local one.

It was my first CT, so I didn't realize that it was odd when the radiologist doing the testing came into the room to ask which ear had the loss. I told him it was the right side; he looked puzzled and mumbled something in which I caught the word 'backward', and returned to his observation room. When he came in a second time with the same question, I was sure I had reason to worry, and I'm not a worrier by nature.

When the radiologist asked me to go into the waiting room to talk, I knew this was not normal doctor action. He told me that he had found a walnut-sized tumor in the LEFT, the good hearing ear, and that there was probably one on the right too that he couldn't see.

Blessed with a very pro-active family, they went to work, contacting everyone they knew about the best doctor for von Recklinghausen (the name for NF2 in many places at that time). A local doctor expressed confidence in his ability to do the surgery, but many, many referrals came in with just a single name, a doctor several hundred miles from my home in the San Francisco Bay Area.

I went to that doctor, one who had a staff member concede to me that while the doctor's bedside manner left something to be desired, he had the surgical hands of a magician. After agonizing about whether to have complete surgical removal and total deafness or partial removal in an attempt to preserve some hearing. I chose to take it all, but not with a whole lot of confidence. So that's when the doctor recommended that I reconsider. I did reconsider, and had only a partial removal.

Some hearing in the low frequencies was preserved. After adding a hearing aid, it was enough to help me lip-read, but not enough for me to discriminate speech without visual input, too. Over the ensuing ten years, the doctor and I did watch and wait and the VS continued to re-grow pretty slowly.

I felt the isolation typical of someone new to NF2. I not only had never met anyone with the syndrome, I had never even heard of it before. Thank goodness the local deaf social services agency, DCARA, had an angel waiting for me in Edna Shipley-Connor, their late deaf counselor. She introduced me to a couple of other NF2ers and other late deaf folks, dramatically reducing my feelings of isolation.

During that time, I tried to return to my third grade classroom and realized I didn't have sufficient residual hearing to continue there. I sought teachers' disability and by the time it was approved - after their audiologist tested me determined to prove I was faking it (and obviously failing to prove that) - it had become necessary to sell my modest townhouse for a small loss, and return to my parents' house with my wife and two toddlers.

I took some graduate classes toward an administrative credential and survived on the kind note-sharing of my classmates. Fortunately, at that time I also went through extensive testing through the California Vocational Rehabilitation office, and they were able to offer to send me back to school. So, my family and I left my parents' house and I returned to college some seven years after my BA, taking a three year course, and earning my MA and credential to teach deaf children. We did that while struggling to make ends meet on disability pay that finally began after months of waiting.

I began college once again some ten months after surgery, having reached the bargaining stage of grieving. "If I have to go to this college as a deaf guy, I'm going to be the best damned deaf student they ever saw." I did and I was, getting much better grades than as an undergraduate and earning the faculty's respect for my learning. I learned sign language in earnest, after having begun in small doses after diagnosis, and thrived academically.

While there, I think my personal grieving showed in my not making many friends. Many people were helpful, most notably a professor of audiology and the three teachers in communicative disorders (my area). But in retrospect, my drive to excel at school cost me too much time from my family. Knowing then what I know now, I would have let my grades slide some and been a person more.

The ten years following that initial partial removal led to my new degree, a third child, and after some personal struggles, to a new teaching position in a full inclusion program, in which I team taught an elementary school classroom that merged deaf and hard of hearing (DHH) kids and hearing kids. My teaching teammates were always hearing and could sign.

Also in that ten years, my residual hearing slowly faded to none, and I had come to terms with my deafness. I knew that I was neither my deafness nor my NF2, but they were parts of the whole me. A lifelong quiet, sensitive person, I found my love of reading hugely valuable since in a book I could understand all the dialogue. As one of those folks who always saw himself as the one who helps others, it was THE tough lesson in becoming deaf for me to learn to ask for help in useful ways. A while after the original discomfort of asking I realized that many people like to be helpful, so that oddly enough, by asking for help in a clear way, others benefitted, too!

I grew to love quotations, the first one that inspired me to find more was this one:

"God has allowed him to have a hearing loss to remind people that we are all distinguished by the challenges we face. If we accept them, even appreciate them, we can inspire and encourage one another in ways that would not be possible in a perfect, complacent world."
(Kathy Long)

Since then I have found many more that are inspiring, about attitude or deafness, or about other things I find relevant or interesting.

After ten years of watch and wait, the doctor said the left VS had grown to 4 cm and needed to be removed. The surgery from hell resulted, a tumor really 5 cm invading my brainstem; a planned eleven day hospital stay turned into nearly a hundred, with two times of mortal danger, pneumonia and infection, facial paralysis on the left side and becoming disabled, needing to learn to swallow, walk and talk again, none of which is quite right now, among other things. Having learned my lessons about changes with my deafness, I think that my internal comfort with who I am helped me heal and keep a pretty even keel. I felt proud when a visitor told me of a rehab hospital staff member's gushing about my great attitude!

I was able to return to the classroom some six months after surgery, greatly weakened. I continued teaching for seventeen more years before accepting disability retirement in 2011. There were more life changes during that time; my second marriage, my children's becoming adults (and yes, discovery that I had passed on the NF2 gene), a successful Gamma Knife on my right VS, co-founding the NF2 Crew, several spectacular hearing dogs, including the one I've trained myself since retiring, and more.

In retrospect, I am deeply grateful to my family and the people in my life who see ME, not my disabilities or deafness. The great serendipities of life awe me; having children too young, but being healthy enough to enjoy them as they grew up, the lessons of change in life, being able to learn enough from my first loss to deal with later ones, and the having the intestinal fortitude instilled by my parents that allows me to keep going.

Now I read a lot, take my hearing dog who doubles as a certified therapy dog to libraries and school, play Scrabble, garden, exercise to try to be prepared for falling with my crummy balance, and hang around my computer entirely too much.

A last thought:

> **"I am not afraid of storms, for I**
> **am learning how to sail my ship."**
> (Louisa May Alcott)

42. Sue Taylor

Sue Taylor, from Warwickshire, UK, was diagnosed with NF2 at the age of 29, she is now 36 years of age. Sue's journey with NF2 begins after the birth of her two children which, combined, caused a unique set of challenges.

In her story Sue talks about her experience as a parent with NF2 and the difficult decision to test her young children for the condition. Sue is hopeful for a brighter future and having found a sense of balance in life with NF2 states that her good days certainly outweigh the bad.

My name is Sue. I was diagnosed with NF2 in May 2006 when I was 29 years old. I am a spontaneous mutation, first in the family.

Until I was diagnosed I led a normal, happy life. I spent my teens and early twenties partying and having a lot of fun and working at a pathology lab. I started to notice a few lumps and bumps and had a schwannoma removed from my left upper arm in 1998 but this was treated in its own right and NF2 was never even considered at this point, I suppose because of its rarity. I then had my first child in 2000 and settled down to a happy home life (although still enjoying a good party!).

In 2004 I married Ian and soon became pregnant with Ben who was born in 2005, so life was going to plan. Being diagnosed changed my life. 2006 became a really hard year! I suddenly had lots of different emotions to deal with (from anger, to fear to panic and anxiety) as well as the physical aspects I knew I was going to be facing. I had my first operation in the July to remove a large meningioma from my brain stem. Surgery went well and I was back home to my young family in 2 weeks. In 2008 I had a second large meningioma removed which was so close to my left acoustic neuroma that I also had my acoustic debulked. This operation went extremely well and I was home doing homework with my oldest son after five days!

During this time I had to deal with the physical effects of NF2. Not only did my hearing begin to deteriorate but my balance started to be a problem and the chronic stiffness from the operations never went away, as well as feeling extremely tired some days.

In 2009 I had Gamma knife radio surgery at a hospital in the north on my debulked acoustic neuroma to stop it growing. The team there were fantastic and it was a painless procedure for me. It has worked but I have lost the hearing on my left side now.

I wear a hearing aid on my right side and am doing my second year lip reading which is hard but great to be around others with hearing loss. Being in noisy busy places like a pub or Asda can be difficult. I often prefer my hubby to do the shopping and I have a girls' night at mine! I do feel it's made me old before my time but I want to be happy and comfortable not silly and anxious because I can't hear. I have good friends that make sure I don't miss out on the gossip!

Initially, after all that had happened, as well as the realisation that this is forever had a knock on effect on my confidence and self esteem and in turn I had bouts of depression. But with the support of my loving family and close friends, and being able to get in touch with the NF2 nurses with any worries or concerns, I have learnt how to manage this and have strategies in place to get through it.

All of this meant that I could no longer work. I had two very bad years trying to cope with not being able to work anymore due to balance problems, constant pain and hearing difficulties. So, I decided to set up my own business! I breed mini lop rabbits. It is a great success and has given me my confidence back. It has given me real purpose and the rabbits don't care if I can't hear them! It keeps me busy as my boys are now at school and I'm not just mum anymore. If I'm tired I can have a rest day as I'm my own boss and I really enjoy it!

When I was first diagnosed I was under several services at various places, which was very difficult to manage. However, I recently got on the patient list at just one hospital which means I have all my appointments (audiologist, opthomology, genetics and surgery team) under one roof which is much more manageable. I have an annual MRI scan and from that we make a plan for that year. I am pleased to say that I am at a 'watch and wait' stage at present. All my other meningiomas are small and my right acoustic neuroma is growing at a slow rate. I still hate the MRI scans, but as long as I take my Kylie CD and wear my sleeping mask I'm fine!

I did not know I had NF2 when I had my children but once diagnosed my geneticist told me about the 50/50 chance that my sons would inherit NF2 from me. In 2008 my oldest son was tested and he came back negative. I can remember screaming down the phone I was so relieved and pleased. I think I deafened my genetics doctor!

In 2010 I asked the team I am under to test my youngest son. As he was only 5 my NF2 nurse came to the house and took a saliva test. He thought it was great fun! It was December and I knew the results would not be ready until the January as saliva tests take longer than blood tests but we did not want to upset him with a blood test so didn't mind the extra wait.

In my heart of hearts I knew that he would be positive as he has a few neurofibromas on his body, like I did as a young child so in a way I was prepared for the news. Sure enough, in mid January 2010 we got the phone call. My youngest son has NF2. For me, this has been very hard as he's too young to be told and we still want him to have a normal childhood. I felt like I needed to know if my children had NF2 but we are all different and others may not want to know at such a young age. Regrets of finding out? Yes sometimes but if it means he can be treated more successfully and not have to have the operations that I've had to have then I know I made the right decision. It is about making an informed choice.

Being a mum is the hardest job in the world! So being a mum and having NF2 is extra hard! I get low because I want the energy to go swimming and do all the fun things, but my sons understand I can't which is not fair on them but they say we love you the way you are. They cope so well as my hearing has dropped so much in their lives. It's frustrating for us all, but we are a family and we help each other and stick together! It's my sons that keep me going and I love them very much.

I have high hopes that there will one day be a cure. Maybe not in my lifetime but I am convinced there will be a cure for my sons!

I get by and I am known to be very positive and I have learnt to live with my NF2. This has taken time but I got here by the support of my family and friends and my own positivity. My good days certainly outweigh the bad.

I have found my NF2 nurses amazing. If I have any worries or concerns they are always there for me and will visit me at home when I have been at my lowest points.

You are unique and everyone's NF2 story is so different. Remember, even though this is a rare condition there are so many people out there to help. Know that you have the right to seek it and it will help.

43. Susanne Rees

Susanne Rees was diagnosed with NF2 at the age of 19, she is now 27 years of age and from Northamptonshire, UK. In 2011 Susanne founded iDID Adventure (www.ididadventure.co.uk); a community interest company aimed at improving physical and mental health through access and participation in adventure sports.

Susanne stresses the importance of goal setting in life, both inside and outside of NF2, and through her journey proves that if the mountains were smooth they'd be impossible to climb.

I was 19 years old when I was diagnosed with NF2; having had no-one in the family with the condition, no real signs of hearing loss or physical difficulty, it came as somewhat of a shock to discover that my neck ache was actually a tumour.

It is difficult to describe the feeling when you are diagnosed with NF2. I know people will have different experiences but I felt numb. After crying at the initial shock, I felt kind of emotionless. I trawled through various websites in search of positive information but it was all either a) medical jargon I didn't understand or b) about NF1... I was desperate to look for positivity!

Like so many, I was the first in the family to have NF2 so I'd never met anyone else with it. This was possibly the scariest thing for me and for the first few years, I didn't want to – I was scared that I would meet someone who'd been through surgeries and lost their hearing and I didn't want to face that; I was still very much in denial. I made the decision not to try and meet any other NF2 patients.

I have to say, the year I was diagnosed was both the best and worst year of my life! I was diagnosed in the April after discovering a large tumour at the top of my spinal cord, and was booked for surgery with only 40% successful recovery rate in August. My surgeon gave me the option to have the operation when I wanted and I figured that if there was a chance I would be paralysed or worse, I want to have seen a bit more of the world first.

My health was much to be desired and as a result of the tumour causing pressure on my brain, I was nauseous and fatigued. My balance was shocking and as soon as I woke I'd spend a lot of time trying not to be sick, which in turn made me feel worse. I didn't want this to be how I would spend the next four months of my life so I made the decision not to let this 'morning sickness' hold me back. I began to incorporate it into my routine (sounds crazy I know). I would wake, be dizzy, get hot sweats, then allow myself to be sick, get fresh air for 15 minutes and be on with my day. It helped me to treat my health as part of my routine so I felt in control of it. I think this was what set the tone for my attitude towards NF2 in the future. NF2 doesn't define me but it is part of who I am.

I continued with work because I needed something 'normal' and took time off before I went for surgery so I could see a bit of the world. I travelled to the east coast of Australia, Malaysia, Italy, New York and made damn sure I could tick off as many items from my 'must see' list as I could. Obviously, in such a short space of time and being really ill, you can't see everything but this was just the beginning...

I almost feel a great appreciation for the time before my surgery; it's quite a powerful thing to reflect on your life. I thought about death and my life so far – for me, it was a huge awakening and I believe that it has contributed to how I cope with other things related and unrelated to NF2 in my life. Through this, I no longer feared change. I think the most important thing, for me anyway, was to take control of my everyday life and prepare for times when NF2 popped up to interrupt.

All I remember after my first surgery was the doctor asking me to wiggle my fingers and toes… nearly everything worked – and I was high on Morphine… result!

Whilst the surgery was a huge success, in the short term, I was paralysed from the surgery. Due to the 'nerve concussion' (I still don't know any medical terms, 8 years on!) I wasn't able to walk and had to have intensive physiotherapy. I won't lie, this was a really, really long road and I decided to set myself a target (in hindsight it was a bit too optimistic bearing in mind I couldn't walk) – I was going to do the three peaks challenge to raise money for an NF2 charity!

Creating targets was the best thing I could do and it really helped me to visualise recovery. I'm not going to lie, it was one of the hardest things I've had to do in my life but whilst I spent so long in hospital and rehabilitation units, it allowed me to really focus in my mind about my recovery. A reward system really worked for me and I couldn't recommend it enough. Just the simple things - my favourite chocolates were peanut M&M's and I would go through at least a big pack a day. My mum would only ever let me eat them if I could pick them up out of a bowl myself. Also, if I worked really hard, my brother would bring me domino's pizza or KFC… they say it's the little things in life.

Months went by, and I gradually got better. Before I knew it, I was back at work and about to take on the three peaks challenge. I wish I could inspire everyone and say how it was a fantastic experience that changed my life… I can't. It was painful, cold and my nerve pain got so bad I had to stop after the first mountain (there is the penalty for exaggerated optimism). I achieved one mountain and for me, that was more than enough – it was nine months following my surgery and I certainly proved my own point. As you can tell, I'm pretty stubborn.

A couple of years went by until a yearly scan showed that my right acoustic neuroma was growing. It was at an ideal size for Gamma-knife Radiosurgery, so my neurosurgeon organised to have another scan six months later to check on it. The second scan came and the tumour had become more aggressive; I was now in a situation where I had to have another major surgery. The surgery to remove an acoustic neuroma damages the auditory nerve and can leave the patient with no hearing in that ear. Sometimes, surgeons will implant an Auditory Brainstem Implant as a 'sleeper' (meaning they'll use it if/when you lose the hearing in the other ear) in the same surgery. This is what they planned for me.

There were very frustrating funding issues from my local authority to pay for the implant and the process to get me into surgery was delayed by around nine months. This had implications of its own as my health began to decline until finally I was rushed into hospital and subsequently had surgery without the ABI. Following my surgery I contracted meningitis, which damaged the hearing in my other ear. Again, the tumour was successfully removed but it had caused facial palsy which resulted in some sight issues. But once again, I focused on my recovery in hospital and spent as much time as I could on physiotherapy exercises for my face... seriously, stick to them.

As with my previous surgery, I was keen to get back to work and 'normality', however, life had other plans. The hearing I expected to come back never did and I was made redundant from my job.

I was struggling to visualise my recovery on this surgery. I realised that all my work experience was in customer services and management; all of which required me to use a phone. I could no longer do this so I genuinely thought I had to completely rethink my career. I decided to set a new target: go to university and train to be a drama teacher.

The road to recovery is never easy but the strength we accrue along the way makes us extraordinary human beings.

Firstly, I took an access to higher education course to gain the qualifications I needed and applied myself ten times more than I ever did at school. This was a great recovery process for me as I realised what I was capable of. Whilst I was at college my left acoustic neuroma started growing and I had Gamma-knife Radiosurgery to treat it. Having Gamma-knife is like having an MRI with a big helmet on. They attach it very tightly so you are given pain relief but other than that it is painless. The side effects of the treatment are quite delayed and so it meant that my symptoms appeared at the same time as my exams!

I passed my course with distinctions in most subjects and was overjoyed to be accepted at Reading University on a theatre and education degree. After my first year, I didn't feel as though I was being challenged or that I was on the right course. I think I felt that I had settled for a course that incorporated deaf studies because I perceived it as the easy option. Rather than pushing to achieve something I really wanted, I'd settled for something that wasn't really me. In the summer between my first and second year I took part in a leadership course by Common Purpose for disabled students. It really put everything in to perspective for me. For the first time I met other disabled people and it completely changed my own perception of disability.

I realised that because of my experience with NF2, I'd began to settle for less than I wanted. Mostly, this was because I was scared I wouldn't be capable of achieving what I wanted. If life has taught me anything it is that everyone is capable of doing whatever they want. Even if the end result is the same, the journey will always be different!

Before I went to university, I had experienced issues trying to take part in Rock Climbing. It was felt that health and safety would get in the way because I couldn't hear. I took this as fact and accepted that I couldn't go climbing now that I was deaf. I found that a lot of disabled people I knew had similar experiences – also some fellow NF2ers. When I was in Reading the climbing centre there was fantastic and really encouraged me as a deaf person. Slowly, I started climbing more regularly and I wanted to do something to change the misperception and find a way to teach both professionals and disabled people that adventurous sports are completely possible for them. Further to climbing, I started taking part in other adventure sports and found they were actively improving my health both mentally and physically… I felt alive!

This is why, in 2011, I founded iDID Adventure; a community interest company aimed at improving physical and mental health through access and participation in adventure sports. The idea initially started with a website offering information about how to adapt a variety of sports to the needs of various disabilities. The business has gone from strength to strength and is now a leading provider of adapted action sport events and adventure programmes for deaf and disabled individuals. Since its launch, iDID has introduced people with a range of disabilities to sports such as Rock Climbing, Wakeboarding, Skiing, Surfing and various other activities.

> **"At any given moment you have the power to say:**
> **this is not how the story is going to end."**
> (Christine Mason Miller)

I'm now profoundly deaf, the director of a company, and use the phone all the time, with the support of a Lip-speaker through Access to Work. I'm involved with some fantastic national organisations to empower deaf and disabled young adults. One thing I've learned is to never apologise for my disability. Get the right communication support for you and follow whatever path you want to… usually the only person stopping you, is you.

44. Will Davidson

Will Davidson is 25 years of age and from London. In his story Will talks about his experience of how losing his hearing at university made things difficult, but not impossible. Despite his challenges with NF2 Will has secured himself a job and is looking forward to the opportunities of the future.

I am 25 years old, I have an amazing job, I love walking, photography, travelling, hanging out with my girlfriend and friends. Oh yeah and I have NF2.

I was diagnosed during my year out between school and starting university, just four days before I was supposed to fly out to Peru to go travelling. Everything happened so quickly that the news didn't have time to sink in. Within three weeks I was having surgery to remove an acoustic neuroma and an ABI fitted.

At that stage I wasn't too bothered about it; in my mind it was about recovering from the operation, enjoying my summer and starting university as normal. I spent a crazy six weeks of my summer backpacking around Europe with some friends and running with the bulls in Pamplona. I felt things were back on track, I was looking forward to starting university.

I started university studying politics and international relations. I was really enjoying the social life and the course, but by Easter I was starting to struggle to hear in lectures, as well as out and about with friends. I really struggled, trying to kid myself and others that I could hear. Four months later I could no longer hear anything. I was told at Christmas during my second year I needed the other acoustic neuroma out. I decided to wait until the summer so that I could deal with it at the end of the university year, have summer to recover, and then carry on.

I remember going to the university's support office and telling them that I needed help, and them turning around and saying 'that's fine, what support do u want?' At the time I had no idea what support I needed, but I realised very quickly that you need to be very strong and confident in explaining what you want and need.

The last year was the hardest year and most isolating. I didn't know how to deal with having no hearing and I struggled through that year. I considered dropping out hundreds of times, but I didn't. I was lucky to have close friends and family to give me the support and encouragement I needed. I was determined, and never gave up.

I am hugely proud that I completed my degree at university. I'm also really proud of the range of jobs that I have had since - working for an MP, the advocacy and lobbying side of charity work, and getting onto a massive telecommunication company's graduate programme. I love being a part of something so huge. There's so much to learn and different areas to work in. There's so much variety and opportunities that I wouldn't get elsewhere.

While things have not always been easy, my challenges with NF2 have really shown me that there are always ways to overcome the obstacles I face. Never accept no for an answer and don't be scared to ask for help. There's a lot of help available, whether it's the disability advisor at college/university or through Access to Work. There are also a lot of charities, both local and national, that will lend you a hand.

Conclusion

"Don't cry because it's over, smile because it happened."
(Mahatma Gandhi)

How on Earth do you write a conclusion to that?! I think that I could spend a lifetime searching for the appropriate words to follow those forty-four incredible stories and would still never find them. I think I will start by saying that it has been an absolute honour to produce this book and to get to know the people involved. It has been the most incredible experience for me; it has taught me so much and has led me to meeting some very special people.

It has also been an emotional journey and a very difficult one at times, especially when I had to face major surgery in the middle of it all. But the people who have shared their stories in this book kept me going, even though they may not know it. Every time I received a new story during my recovery their attitudes and determination to persevere against all the odds motivated me and drove me forward. They lifted my spirits when I needed it most and when I thought they could not be lifted.

I developed the *Can You Hear Us?* project as a way of giving a voice to people with NF2, and *NF2: Our Journeys* has achieved just that. My idea was born through inspiration and with the vision of inspiring others to seek the good in bad situations. This book has many objectives, but my ultimate hope for the book is to be a resource and a guide for those whose heads and hearts have become heavy and burdened with the poison of fear and isolation.

This book does not hide the fact that life with NF2 can be tough, but it also shows that NF2 can make us stronger. We show that although sometimes we do lose things we also gain things and together we stand as proof that it is possible to live a happy and fulfilled life despite the challenges that NF2 can bring.

I have worked tirelessly and passionately on this project for over a year and it feels strange that it has all now come to an end, but I am looking forward to witnessing and being a part of the rewards and opportunities that this book will bring to us all. The book has become a positive part of all of our journeys and I know that, really, this is just the beginning.

Although I have been the individual with the task of gathering these stories and producing this book, I do not in the slightest view this book as my book. This is everyone's book, and it is something that we can all take pride in, for these are *Our Journeys.*

So we have come to the end of the book, what now? Well, that's up to you. We cannot tell you where to go, we can only show you where we have been. We have shown you some of the paths there are to walk and now you must choose your way. But do not be fearful for we are here, and remember, if you need one, a friend is always near.

So what are your ideas? What are your dreams?

Whatever they are know that this is just the beginning and that regrets are hard to mend, so don't ever give up on what you want and love, because to be defeated is the end.

Jessica

Quotations

I wanted to include a selection of some of my favourite quotations that I have collected over the years. They have helped me tremendously in times of doubt, either about myself or the world around me, and have played a part in helping me to understand some important life lessons. I am also an admirer of the way that some people can sum up a point in just one or two sentences and potentially change how you view things. Some of the introductions I wrote for each story in this book have been inspired by these thought-provoking quotes so I therefore felt it was necessary to reference them. Hope you enjoy.

"One of life's greatest lessons is learning how to be happy, how you spend your day is actually how you spend your life and in the end, it's not the years in your life that count – it's the life in your years"
(Abraham Lincoln)

"When writing the story of your life, don't let anyone else hold the pen"
(Anon)

"For every disability you have, you are blessed with more than enough abilities to overcome your challenges"
(Nick Vujicic)

"There is so much in the world for us all if only we have the eyes to see it, and the heart to love it, and the hand to gather it to ourselves"
(Lucy Maud Montgomery)

"Know that your worst fears could just as
easily prove to be your best surprise"
(Nick Vujicic)

"Defeat only happens to those who refuse to try again"
(Nick Vujicic)

"The best and most beauliful things in life cannot
be seen, not touched, but are felt in the heart"
(Helen Keller)

"Life isn't measured by the breaths we take but
the moments that take our breathe away"
(Anon)

"Life doesn't give you the people you want.
It gives you the people you need:
to help you, to hurt you, to love you, to leave you
and to make you the person you were meant to be"
(Anon)

"You can easily judge the character of a man by
how he treats those who can do nothing for him"
(James D.Miles)

"Don't take anything personally. Nothing you do is
because of you. What others say and do is a projection
of their own reality, their own dream. When you are
immune to the opinions and actions of others, you
won't be the victim of needless suffering"
(Don Miguel Ruiz)

"Work for a cause, not for applause.
Live life to express, not to impress.
Don't strive to make your presence noticed,
just make your absence felt"
(Anon)

"Don't cry because it's over,
smile because it happened"
(Mahatma Gandhi)

"Tempering a sunny disposition with a small dose of
realism or even pessimism might be the best way to
build resilience and achieve one's goals"
(Anon)

"The best feeling in the world is seeing someone smile
and knowing you were the reason why"
(Anon)

"There are only two days in the year that nothing can be
done. One is called yesterday and one is called tomorrow, so
today is the right day to love, believe, do, and mostly live"
(His Holiness The Dalai Lama)

"Always be a first-rate vision of yourself, instead
of a second-rate version of someone else"
(Judy Garland)

"The two greatest days of your life are the day
you were born and the day you found out why"
(Darlene Zschech)

"You gain strength, courage, and confidence by every experience in which you really stop to look fear in the face"
(Eleanor Roosevelt)

"To the world you may just be one person, but to one person you may just be the world"
(Brandi Snyder)

"The only person better than you is the person you've yet to become"
(Juliet Dillinger)

"Believe in yourself and all that you are. Know that there is something inside of you that is greater than any obstacle"
(Christian D.Larson)

"The best thing to hold onto in life is each other"
(Audrey Hepburn)

"Be who you are and say what you feel because those who mind don't matter and those who matter don't mind"
(Dr Suess)

"The future belongs to those who believe in the beauty of their dreams"
(Eleanor Roosevelt)

"Opportunities are like sunrises. If you wait too long, you miss them"
(Anon)

"Life shrinks and expands in
proportion to one's courage"
(Anais Nin)

"Your talent is God's gift to you.
What you do with it is your gift back to God"
(Leo Buscaglia)

"Good people bring out the good in other people"
(Anon)

"Just do once what others say you can't and you
will never pay attention to their limitations again"
(Captain James Cook)

"If the mountains were smooth
they'd be impossible to climb"
(Anon)

"At any given moment you have the power to say:
this is not how the story is going to end"
(Christine Mason Miller)

"If you begin looking at each breath as a blessing, then
suddenly everything in an ordinary life becomes a miracle"
(Kirsti A.Dyer)

"I alone cannot change the world, but I can cast
a stone across the waters to create many ripples."
(Mother Teresa)

Resources

This is a list of charities and organisations that either directly support people with NF2 and their families or offer services that will be useful for people with NF2 and their families. There are many more organisations out there to research into and new ones coming into existence regularly. Direction to further resources can be found on most of the featured websites in this section. If your NF2 care is based in England, your NF2 specialist nurse will also be able to direct you to resources.

Action on Hearing Loss
information@hearingloss.org.uk
www.actiononhearingloss.org.uk
Action on Hearing Loss is the charity working for a world where hearing loss doesn't limit or label people, where tinnitus is silenced – and where people value and look after their hearing. They provide care, support and information; raise awareness of hearing loss issues; campaign and lobby to change public policy; and fund research into a cure for hearing loss and tinnitus.

Advocure NF2 Inc. (USA)
contact@advocurenf2.org
www.advocurenf2.org
Advocure NF2 is a non-profit public charity focused on advocacy and research solely for NF2. An all-volunteer organisation which has no administrative costs. The website www.advocurenf2.org and the quarterly newsletter 'The Compass' focus on cutting edge research and developments regarding NF2. 'The Compass' has a wide distribution to the research community.

British Tinnitus Association (BTA) (UK)
Telephone : 0114 250 9933
Textphone : 0114 258 5694
info@tinnitus.org.uk
www.tinnitus.org.uk
British Tinnitus Association is a world leader in providing support and advice about tinnitus. We provide accurate, reliable and authoritative information, much of it written by medical professionals or clinical researchers.

Can You Hear Us? (UK)
nf2awarenessuk@hotmail.co.uk
www.canyouhearus.co.uk
facebook page: http://on.fb.me/16znkuj or search for us on facebook
Can You Hear Us? is a social advocacy group on a mission to prove that there is more to life than NF2 through the uniting and presenting of people who refuse to be defined by the disease. Can You Hear Us? has been developed as a way of giving a voice to people with NF2 and to encourage those with the condition to take advantage of adversity.

Changing Faces (UK)
info@changingfaces.org.uk
www.changingfaces.org.uk
Changing Faces is a charity for people and families who are living with conditions, marks or scars that affect their appearance. We aim to help individuals lead full, confident and satisfying lives and to transform public attitudes towards people with an unusual appearance.

Children with Tumours (UK)
info@childrenwithtumours.org
www.childrenwithtumours.org
Children With Tumours is a UK charity set up to support children through building confidence and giving hope. We achieve this in a number of ways, including the provision of camps where strong friendships are made, through research to help with their condition, through awareness campaigns to develop the understanding of others and through creating a safe social framework through which our children and grow and develop.

Hearing Link (UK)
Tel: 0300 111 1113
Text/SMS: 07526 12355
enquiries@hearinglink.org
www.hearinglink.org/nf2programmes
www.hearinglink.org/usefulorgs
Hearing Link is a UK charity that specialises in hearing loss issues. It provides information and support to people diagnosed with NF2 who are experiencing a change in their ability to hear, or have other associated symptoms such as balance problems or tinnitus (ringing or noises in the ear). Hearing Link also runs highly regarded five-day residential courses for people who have NF2 and their families - these are known as 'Intensive Rehabilitation Programmes'. They are informative, helpful and uplifting.

IDID Adventure (UK)
info@ididadventure.co.uk
www.ididadventure.co.uk
iDID Adventure is an award winning social, enterprise improving confidence, self-esteem and health through access and participation in adventure sports. IDID provide events and adventure programmes for deaf and disabled individuals and have successfully introduced a wide range of people to sports including rock climbing, canoeing, skiing, wakeboarding and surfing.

Make-A-Wish Foundation (UK)

info@make-a-wish.org.uk

www.make-a-wish.org.uk

Make a wish Foundation has a very simple objective – to grant magical wishes to children and young people fighting life-threatening conditions. There are more than 20,000 children in the UK living with life-threatening conditions. We believe that every one of them deserves to experience the magic of a Make-A-Wish wish – and they are truly magical. A small and dedicated team of professional wish granters works alongside hundreds of volunteers to turn our children's wishes into reality. Whether a wish is to be a princess or a train driver for the day, own the latest TV or computer equipment, meet a favourite celebrity or just enjoy some special time away from home with their family, a wish come true brings so much to a child's life and provides memories that last a lifetime for the whole family.

NDCS (The National Deaf Children's Society) (UK)

helpline@ndcs.org.uk

www.ndcs.org.uk

NDCS is the leading charity dedicated to creating a world without barriers for deaf children and young people.

NF2 Awareness UK Facebook group

nf2awarenessuk@hotmail.co.uk

facebook page: http://on.fb.me/16znkuj or search for us on facebook

NF2 Awareness UK is the Facebook group associated with Can You Hear Us? connecting and supporting those living with NF2 in the UK.

NF2IS (Neurofibromatosis Type 2 Information & Services) (USA)

lori@nf2is.org
www.nf2is.org
Supporting the NF2 Community through sharing Medical Information and Services. NF2IS has a very useful list of NF2 organisations throughout the world which is kept up to date: *http://nf2is.org/nf_worldwide.php*

NF2UK Yahoo Email Group (UK)

Nf2UK-subscribe@yahoogroups.com
NF2UK Yahoo email group is for families affected by NF2. NF2 can be a very isolating condition so the group aims to offer support and provide an opportunity for discussion about all things related to NF2. To subscribe contact via email.

Sense (UK)

info@sense.org.uk
www.sense.org.uk
Sense is a national charity that supports and campaigns for children and adults who are deafblind. Vision: a world in which all deafblind children and adults can be full and active members of society. Purpose: to support and promote the interests of people who are deafblind, multi-sensory-impaired, or who have a single sensory impairment with additional needs.

The Children's Tumor Foundation (USA)

info@ctf.org
www.ctf.org
The Children's Tumor Foundation is dedicated to improving the health and well-being of individuals and families affected by neurofibromatosis (NF), the term for three distinct disorders: NF1, NF2 and schwannomatosis.

The Ear Foundation

info@earfoundation.org.uk
www.earfoundation.org.uk
The Ear Foundation provides independent information, education and support for deaf children, young people and adults with cochlear implants and other technologies, their families and their supporting professionals. We also carry out child and family-centred research in the field of cochlear implantation and other hearing technologies.

The Neuro Foundation (UK)

info@nfauk.org
www.nfauk.org
The Neuro Foundation is the authoritative voice of Neurofibromatosis in the UK. Our vision is to improve the lives of those with Neurofibromatosis Type 1 and Type 2 in the UK. We achieve this by providing first class information, support and advice; facilitating and promoting innovative research, and being an advocate for those with Neurofibromatosis.

The Willow Foundation (UK)

info@willowfoundation.org.uk
www.willowfoundation.org.uk
The Willow Foundation is a national charity that provides special days for seriously ill 16 to 40 year olds. Every special day aims to provide beneficiaries and their loved ones with a break from the realities of their diagnosis and treatment. At a time of uncertainty, spending quality time with family and friends can help restore a sense of normality, boost confidence and create precious memories for the future.

Acknowledgements

"Gratitude is the memory of the heart."
(Jean Baptiste Massieu)

With thanks and highest praise to Julie Baker, Gabriela Bazan, Bethany, Katie Brady, Craig Briscoe, Julie Broome, Beka Chanturia, Claire, Peter Crawshaw, David, Will Davidson, Krissy Diaz, Mark Dickson, Matt Hay, Michelle Jesberg, Sally Kingsley, Anna Lickley, Halina M.X., Jan McGovern, Claire Middleton, Adam Murdey, Natalie, Marianne Oliva, Joanne Page, Melinda Pinkerton, Poetgirl, Mark Ramsey, Susanne Rees, Sally Richards, Ben Ryan, Robert Sebastian, Shaunna, Steve Silverman, Jessica Stone, Keith Straker, Fred Suter, Bruno Tamassia, Sue Taylor and Joanne Ward who all gave their time and contributed their stories to this book.

Your courage to face the challenges of adversity and willingness to help others do the same is truly inspirational.

Celebrate the fact that you are now published authors and that your stories will live on for eternity in *NF2: Our Journeys*.

To the family and friends of all the authors for supporting them in their journeys.

To Tom Guglielmi, Lynda McFaull, Jean H Pless, Anthony O'Shea and the family of Nathalie Trytell who provided the wonderful tributes in this book to lost loved ones in order to keep their spirits alive and inspire others.

The Joe Guglielmi Memorial Fund, The Neuro Foundation, and everyone who raised funds and donated towards the production costs of the book for making it all possible.

To Terence Dalton, Nicholas Hunt, and the rest of the team at The Lavenham Press for taking us smoothly through the production process and making this book become a reality.

To The Neuro Foundation, Children With Tumours, Hearing Link, Children's Tumour Foundation, Advocure NF2, NF2IS, and iDID Adventure for their support in promotion and encouragement.

The specialised NF2 service in England based from Addenbrooke's Hospital Cambridge, John Radcliffe Hospital Oxford, St Mary's Hospital Manchester, Guy's and St Thomas' Hospital London, and other centres throughout the UK for their assistance.

With further thanks to my NF2 Nurse Practitioners Juliette Durie-Gair and Sally Taylor for helping me at any given moment and for encouraging me throughout my journey with this book.

To Darren Osborne for all his hard work and efforts helping me with the creation of the book and all things related to the Can You Hear Us? project. And to his wife Laura, my kindred spirit.

To my faithful family members and wonderful friends for sharing both my suffering and my joy and for never doubting my ability to achieve my dreams even when I doubted it myself.

To Grandad (Pipe) David and Catherine, Nan Elaine and Grandad Eric for always believing that there was something special inside of me. With added appreciation to Nan Elaine for being my guardian and escorting me in my faith.

Finally to my Step-dad Stephen and Mum Wendy for inspiring me to never give up however difficult things may seem and for always being the supreme role models for me to do proud.

"As many people as there are to hold you back,
there are angels whose humanity makes up
for all the others. I've had my share of angels."
(Abraham Verghese)

Your Journey

**"When writing the story of your life,
don't let anyone else hold the pen"**
(Anon)

Now it is your turn to do the talking... Where have you been? Where do you want to go?

NF2 is part of your journey, but we know there is much more. We have provided some blank pages for you to write some notes and make this book personal to you. Add your stories, brainstorm your ideas, recognise your dreams, and/or set yourself goals. Live your life your way, the time is now, begin; this is *Your Journey*.

Your Journey

Your Journey